It's another Quality Book from CGP

*The best way to improve your punctuation in Year 6
(ages 10-11) is by doing as much practice as you can.*

*That's where this book comes in. It's packed with questions
that'll test you on all the tricky punctuation skills, including the
new ones that you'll meet for the first time in Year 6.*

What's more, it's perfectly matched to the new National Curriculum.

What CGP is all about

*Our sole aim here at CGP is to produce the highest quality books
— carefully written, immaculately presented and
dangerously close to being funny.*

*Then we work our socks off to get them out to you
— at the cheapest possible prices.*

Section 1 — Sentence Punctuation

Capital Letters and Full Stops

Sentences always start with a capital letter and often finish with a full stop.
Use capital letters for names of particular people, places or things, and for I.

Tomorrow I am going to Aunt Sarah's wedding.

1 **Rewrite** the sentences below with **capital letters** and **full stops** in the correct places.

the train to manchester takes two hours

....

mr jones married miss newton on 1st july

....

i have a cat it's called meg

....

2 This passage is missing **full stops** and **capital letters**. **Add** full stops in the **correct** places and **circle** the words that should have a **capital letter**.

tomorrow is mr frimley's birthday mr frimley is our teacher we

have planned a surprise party for him at lunchtime everyone is

bringing in something different for us to eat will is making a

cake and i am bringing party hats and streamers i hope the

party is a success it took ages to organise

"I can use capital letters and full stops."

Question Marks and Exclamation Marks

Question marks are always used at the end of questions. ➤ Where are you?

Exclamation marks can be used for commands or to show when something is said loudly or with strong emotion. ➤ He lied to me!

Ellipses can also be used to end a sentence. They are three dots that show an idea is incomplete. ➤ I'm not angry...

1 Draw lines to **match** each sentence to the correct **punctuation mark**.

Those lights look amazing

Do you want me to help you

I enjoy going out for dinner

I don't want to go, but

| ? |
| . |
| ! |
| ... |

2 Use the **punctuation marks** to write **sentences** which include each of these words.

magic tricks   Jimmy   ?

....

rocket   moon   .

....

zombies   garden   !

....

friendly   neighbours   ?

....

"I can use question marks and exclamation marks."

4

Sentence Practice

Remember — sentences must always start with a capital letter. They can end with a full stop, a question mark, an exclamation mark or an ellipsis.

1 Draw lines to **match** each sentence to the correct **punctuation mark**.

I'd like to buy a new car

How far away from the beach are we

What have I done to deserve this

Tom went to the zoo yesterday

Let's try this one next

Yes, we won

Get out of my sight

Did you find them

2 <u>Add</u> the missing punctuation in the <u>boxes</u> below.

"Help ☐ Help ☐ " shouted Sam. A police officer appeared.

"What's the problem, Sir ☐ " he asked.

"I've been robbed ☐ " cried Sam, pointing at a man who was

running up the street ☐

The policeman chased after the thief, and everyone was surprised to see

what happened next ☐

3 Write the most likely <u>final punctuation</u> in each box.

Have you been before ☐

Thank you very much ☐

I can't see anything ☐

Stop that man ☐

Do you want a waffle ☐

I like the green one ☐

Please pass the gravy ☐

Come here, now ☐

Section 1 — Sentence Punctuation

© CGP — not to be photocopied

4 The words in these sentences are all jumbled up. <u>Rewrite</u> the sentences in the <u>correct order</u> and add <u>capital letters</u>, <u>question marks</u> and <u>exclamation marks</u> in the correct places.

homework help can you me with my

....

aliens on roof the landed some have

....

football back when can have I my

....

me the tell right truth now

....

5 <u>Use the words below</u> to help you write your own <u>sentences</u>, each one ending with the piece of punctuation shown.

| crocodile   fly   dragon   teacher   cloud   zebra |

.

....

...

....

?

....

!

....

"I can punctuate sentences correctly."

Section 2 — Commas

Commas in Lists

Use commas to separate items in a list. There should be a comma between each thing in the list except the last two. These two are separated with 'and' or 'or'.

> Bring your swimming trunks, a sun hat and a waterproof jacket.

(1) **Add commas** in the correct places in the passage below.

Yesterday, I went to a theme park with Jordan Carl Elijah and David. We went on three roller coasters a log flume a Ferris wheel and some bumper cars. At lunchtime, we had cheeseburgers with chips big cups of fizzy pop and a chocolate bar each. We left with big smiles full tummies and happy memories.

(2) **Write a list of four things to complete each sentence. Remember to use commas in the correct places.**

My mum bought me ....

....

....

Emily's favourite foods are ....

....

....

In my bedroom, I have ....

....

....

"I can use commas to separate items in a list."

Commas to Join Sentences

Use a **comma** with a **conjunction** to join **main clauses** in a **compound sentence**.

> I wanted a blue sweet. She gave me a red one.
>
> I wanted a blue sweet, but she gave me a red one.

The conjunctions you use after a comma are **for, and, nor, but, or, yet** and **so**.
You can remember them as **FANBOYS**.

1 Add <u>commas</u> in the correct places in the sentences below.

I went to the cinema for it was my birthday.

I've got a new bike so I've started cycling to school.

I bought a ticket for the raffle and I won first prize.

I'll walk through the haunted house or go on the ghost train.

2 Use <u>commas</u> and <u>conjunctions</u> to make <u>three sentences</u>.
Each sentence should use a <u>main clause</u> from each column.

I went on holiday.	I got the train.
My car was broken.	I had a great time.
I baked a cake.	It tasted horrible.

1. ....

2. ....

3. ....

"I can use commas to join main clauses."

Section 2 — Commas

Commas After Subordinate Clauses

Commas **separate** subordinate clauses **from** main clauses **in complex sentences.**
Only use a comma **if the** subordinate clause **comes first.**

subordinate
clause → Once you've laid the table, you can watch TV. ← main
clause

1 Tick the sentences that use <u>commas</u> correctly.

Although he can't dance, my dad is usually quite cool. ☐

The shark had very good teeth since, he brushed them every day. ☐

Even when it's the weekend, I like to have breakfast at 7 am. ☐

2 Match the <u>subordinate clause</u> to the correct <u>main clause</u>. Then write
out the <u>complete sentences</u> with <u>commas</u> in the correct places.

<u>Subordinate Clauses</u>   <u>Main Clauses</u>

As Ben hates coffee   I'd like to swim in the lake.

Before you start eating   we still had fun.

Even though it was raining   you should wash your hands.

Although it is winter   I've made him a hot chocolate.

....

....

....

....

"I can use commas after subordinate clauses."

Commas After Introductions

Use a comma after an adverbial phrase at the beginning of a sentence.
Adverbial phrases tell you where, when, how or how often something happens.

> Next week, I'm going to a music concert.

1 Add <u>commas</u> in the correct places in the sentences below.

For ten minutes Lewis tried to solve the puzzle.

With a big smile Richard greeted his exchange partner.

Every evening I practise the piano.

In Ancient Egypt the rulers were called pharaohs.

On Monday I'm playing tennis for the county.

2 <u>Complete</u> the sentences below by adding <u>main clauses</u>.
Remember to put <u>commas</u> in the correct places.

Before breakfast ....

As quickly as possible ....

Every Wednesday evening ....

In a large bowl ....

At the zoo ....

For twenty minutes ....

"I can use commas after adverbial introductions."

© CGP — not to be photocopied

Section 2 — Commas

Commas for Extra Information

Use commas to separate extra information in a sentence.

Keith and Mike, who'd never met before, got on really well.

The sentence should still make sense when the extra information is removed.

1 Rewrite the sentences, adding in <u>commas</u> where they are needed.

The bun which had lots of icing was delicious.

....

The theme which was films was very popular.

....

Mildred my cat is very fierce.

....

2 Add <u>commas</u> in the <u>correct</u> places in the passage below.

Today on our school trip to the zoo we had a picnic. Nick the youngest boy in our class brought a selection pack of crisps. The salt and vinegar flavoured crisps which are always everyone's favourite went first. Georgina my best friend brought a big box of biscuits. The custard creams which are my favourites were very popular. The digestives a much more boring kind of biscuit were also very popular. We did have some fruit mainly oranges and bananas as well.

3 Rewrite the sentences below adding the <u>extra information</u> in the boxes. Use <u>commas</u> where they are needed.

The competition was won by Mr Smith. (which was very difficult)

....

....

Paris is home to the Eiffel Tower. (the capital of France)

....

....

The fire destroyed the house. (which continued through the night)

....

....

4 Use <u>extra information</u> to complete each sentence. Remember to put <u>commas</u> in the correct places.

My sister ....

is a professional chess player.

My friends ....

always laugh at my singing.

My mum baked apple pie ....

and it was delicious.

The dog ....

ate all of its food straight away.

"I can use commas to separate extra information."

Comma Practice

Commas **are used to separate items in a list**, to join **parts of a sentence**, **to separate** introductions **and to add in** extra information.

(1) **For each of these sentences, add** <u>commas</u> **in the correct places.**

Alan [ ] my boss [ ] has an [ ] excellent sense of humour.

Before [ ] you go [ ] let me [ ] give you your present.

So that [ ] you can find your way [ ] I'll [ ] lend you a torch.

I would [ ] come with you [ ] but [ ] I just don't have time.

Shall I wear [ ] the tie with spots [ ] stripes [ ] or stars?

For [ ] now [ ] let's just [ ] keep doing it like this.

(2) **Match each sentence to the correct** <u>reason</u> **for using** <u>commas</u>.

Like a professional,
he was very polite.

We went to the party,
but it was awful.

Mr Cole, my neighbour,
is amazing at tennis.

As you're here, let's
go through this now.

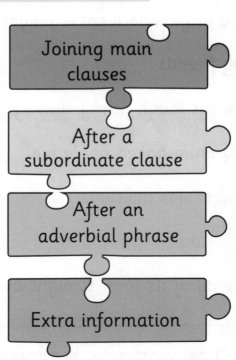

Joining main clauses

After a subordinate clause

After an adverbial phrase

Extra information

3 <u>Read</u> the passage and write in the commas in the correct places.

My football coach Mr Cameron is giving me extra training sessions. He thinks I have potential but my mum thinks I should concentrate more on my schoolwork. Even though I work really hard at school she still thinks that football is a distraction. Before practice she always checks that I have done all of my homework. She checks for messy handwriting spelling mistakes and wrong answers. If I haven't finished my work I can't go to practice.

4 <u>Rewrite</u> each sentence, adding the words in the box in the right place. Remember to use <u>commas</u> correctly.

The race took place today.   (the 100 m sprint)

....

My bike needs repairing.   (which is very old)

....

5 Write a <u>list</u> of four things to complete the sentence. Remember to use <u>commas</u> in the correct places.

If I were rich, I would ....

....

....

"I can use commas correctly."

Section 3 — Brackets and Dashes

Brackets for Extra Information

A pair of brackets (or parentheses) separate extra information in a sentence.

> Brian and George (two tortoises) have lived there for thirty years.

The brackets go around the extra information.

> Andrea can't come (she's away).

The full stop goes after the second bracket.

1 <u>Rewrite</u> each of these sentences, <u>adding</u> a <u>pair of brackets</u> to each one.

The ship a cruise liner left at nine o'clock.

....

Martin Victoria's husband is a professional artist.

....

The snow six feet deep meant we stayed at home.

....

Alan rushed into the café he was desperate for a drink.

....

2 <u>Complete</u> each of these sentences by <u>writing</u> something in the <u>gaps</u> between the brackets.

The school trip (...) was a disaster.

Wendy and Bob were very tired (...).

The farmers (...) went on holiday.

Mike's bedroom (...) is pretty small.

"I can use brackets to add extra information."

Dashes for Extra Information

A pair of dashes adds information in the same way as a pair of brackets.

> Andrea and Caroline — the twin sisters — both play the piano.

1 Each of these sentences needs a <u>pair of dashes</u>. <u>Put</u> them into the <u>correct</u> boxes.

The ☐ whole family ☐ even Sam ☐ is going on holiday.

Niall's pig ☐ the pink ☐ spotty one ☐ loves having mud baths.

Our wedding ☐ seven months ☐ away ☐ will be ☐ on a boat.

The suitcase ☐ bulging ☐ and heavy ☐ wouldn't fit ☐ in the boot.

2 <u>Rewrite</u> each of these sentences in the correct order using a pair of dashes.

> my dog   enjoys chasing squirrels   a German shepherd

....

> travelled to Scotland   an American   Keith's cousin

....

3 <u>Complete</u> each of these sentences by <u>adding</u> something between the dashes.

Dr Katich — .... — arrived at work.

Susannah's car — .... — wouldn't start.

Ray made dinner — .... — in the kitchen.

Tim and Naomi — .... — started laughing.

"I can use dashes to add extra information."   ☺✓ 😐✓ ☹✓

Single Dashes

A **single dash** can be used to separate two clauses.

Eleanor looked in the cupboard — there was a big spider.

The dash creates a **pause** in the middle of the sentence.

(1) Put a <u>tick</u> next to the sentences that have used a dash correctly and put a <u>cross</u> next to the ones that haven't.

Tip — don't use too many dashes in formal writing.

The house was dark — there were no lights on. ☐

Pedro needed — to find the exit quickly. ☐

Everyone was going — to the match last night. ☐

Helen bought three bags of fruit — the apples looked delicious. ☐

(2) Only <u>one</u> of the dashes is needed in each of these sentences. <u>Cross out</u> all of the <u>dashes</u> that aren't needed.

Andy searched the room — Nicole was nowhere — to be seen.

I had steak and chips — for lunch — the steak was excellent.

Keith — stepped outside — it was a cold, frosty morning.

There was — a loud bang — someone had knocked — over the teapot.

(3) <u>Complete</u> each sentence by using a <u>dash</u> to separate <u>two clauses</u>.

Richard stopped suddenly ....

Mike and Simon missed the bus ....

The crocodile was hungry ....

"I can join two clauses using a single dash."

Hyphens

Hyphens **are used to show** which **word an adjective** describes.

> a second-hand torch

a second hand-torch

This is a torch that isn't new.

This 'hand-torch' is not the first. It is the second.

Hyphens are also used to join words **together or add a** prefix. **Some words are written with a hyphen so they aren't** confused **with similar words.**

> I re-covered the sofa. ⟶ **This means that the sofa was** covered again.

> I've recovered from the flu. ⟶ **This means that I** got better **after the flu.**

---

1 **Each of these sentences needs a <u>hyphen</u> adding. <u>Put</u> one into the <u>correct</u> box.**

My bad ☐ tempered ☐ sister ☐ slammed the door.

The price ☐ of a second ☐ class ☐ stamp has risen dramatically.

Kat's long ☐ term ☐ partner doesn't like her ☐ dog.

Sugar ☐ free ☐ doughnuts just don't taste ☐ right.

Our local ☐ restaurant ☐ only serves home ☐ made food.

---

2 **Circle the <u>correct</u> word to complete the sentences so that they make sense.**

Ravi had to <u>research</u> / <u>re-search</u> Henry VIII for his homework.

Our postman forgot to <u>resort</u> / <u>re-sort</u> the letters.

Ed asked Dave for the votes to be <u>re-counted</u> / <u>recounted</u>.

My gran can still <u>recall</u> / <u>re-call</u> the day I was born.

"I know what hyphens do and how to use them."

Section 3 — Brackets and Dashes

Section 4 — Apostrophes

Apostrophes for Missing Letters

Use an apostrophe to show where you've left letters out of a contraction.

they will ➡ they'll	who would ➡ who'd	will not ➡ won't

Sometimes the contraction doesn't quite match the words it's made from.

---

1   <u>Write</u> the <u>words</u> in the <u>boxes</u> into each sentence in their <u>contracted form</u>.

You .... called me as soon as you heard!   [should have]

Jen .... remember where Rupert kept the remote.   [could not]

"This is boring. .... it going to start?" Lizi asked.   [When is]

Ruth wanted to know why .... not been selected.   [she had]

Chris thought .... be fun to start a cricket team.   [it would]

---

2   <u>Rewrite</u> each sentence below.   <u>Change</u> the <u>contractions</u> into their <u>longer versions</u>.

I didn't do it, I promise!   I did not do it, I promise! ....

What're we going to do?   ....

I must've left it behind.   ....

She'll be here soon.   ....

How's your sister doing?   ....

You've made it.   ....

I haven't got a clue.   ....

"I can use apostrophes for missing letters."

Apostrophes for Possession

You can use apostrophes to show that someone or something owns something.

For singular nouns, and plural nouns that don't end in 's', add an apostrophe and 's'. ⟹ the drum's beat   the bus's driver   the mice's hole

If a plural noun ends in 's', you only add the apostrophe. ⟹ the daisies' petals

1 Rewrite each phrase so that it changes from <u>singular</u> to <u>plural</u>.

singular	plural
the bear's paw	the bears' paws
the child's smile	
the gorilla's face	
the cherry's stalk	
the lizard's tongue	

2 Write a sentence about each set of words, using an apostrophe to show possession.

Anne race nine → Anne's race started at nine in the morning.

bear fur pink →

Joe bobsleigh crash →

aliens ship lost →

cactus spikes sharp →

"I can use apostrophes to show possession."

Its and It's

The words 'its' and 'it's' mean two different things.

its This means 'belonging to it'. ⟹ its face is round

it's This means 'it is' or 'it has'. ⟹ it's a boy   it's taken ages

---

1 <u>Write</u> '<u>its</u>' or '<u>it's</u>' to <u>complete</u> the <u>sentences</u> below.

I think .... under the table.

The airline cancelled .... flight.

My dog loves .... bed.

.... been a total disaster!

The chick went to find .... nest.

.... an earthquake — run!

I think .... stopped snowing.

Don't worry, ... going to be fine.

---

2 <u>Circle</u> the <u>incorrect</u> uses of '<u>its</u>' and '<u>it's</u>' in the passage below.

I've just had my book published — it's all about King Arthur and his knights. I'm sure its going to be a bestseller because it's been liked by everyone who's read it so far. It's cover has a picture of the round table, my name and the title in big gold letters. Its going on sale next week — I can't wait!

---

3 <u>Write a sentence</u> about each <u>picture</u> that uses either '<u>its</u>' or '<u>it's</u>'.

....

....

....

....

"I can use the words 'its' and 'it's' correctly."

Apostrophe Practice

You can use apostrophes to show where letters are missing, or to show possession for nouns. Remember that 'its' and 'it's' are two different words.

1 Put a **cross** next to the **sentences** which use **apostrophes incorrectly**. **Write** out the **incorrect words** so that they are **correct**.

This hospital' staff all wear uniform. ☐ ....

Four girls' costumes were left on the floor. ☐ ....

My business' new product is out today. ☐ ....

The lion roared and bared it's sharp teeth. ☐ ....

It's my eleventh birthday in a fortnight. ☐ ....

2 **Add apostrophes** to these **sentences** where they are **needed**.

Are you sure Alisons freckles havent moved?

In Mr Greens opinion, I shouldnt have won.

Grandads hearing wont improve.

Its rained a lot, so the rivers burst its banks.

3 **Write a sentence** using **two apostrophes**: one to **show possession** and one to show a **missing letter**. Use the words in the **box** to **help** you.

Rani   crocodile   swim

....

"I can use apostrophes correctly."

Section 5 — Inverted Commas

Punctuating Speech

Speech always ends with a punctuation mark inside the speech marks, wherever it comes in the sentence.

Fran said, "We love cats."

comma — capital letter — full stop

"Is it time," he asked, "to go home?"

punctuation mark

If the speech is continued, you don't need to start with a capital letter.

---

1 **Tick** the sentences which are **punctuated correctly**.

"This is my favourite cabbage" said Farmer Giles proudly. ☐

"Can you pass me those dirty dishes, please?" asked Harini. ☐

My gran always says, "never judge a book by its cover" ☐

"This," the scientist told us, "is the most deadly jellyfish of all." ☐

"Believe it or not", said the host, "you've won first prize!" ☐

---

2 **Fill** in the **boxes** with the **correct punctuation** to **complete** each **sentence**.

"I am through to the national finals! ☐ cried the gymnast ☐

Erik asked ☐ "How do I say 'good morning' in French ☐ "

Artem yelled as loud as he could, "I've found the secret tunnel ☐ ☐

"I always have a sandwich and an apple for lunch ☐ ☐ Beth said.

The police officer said calmly ☐ "Tell me where the money is ☐ "

Marco put up his hand and asked, ☐ Is the answer seventeen? ☐

"You've lost my magazine, ☐ she said ☐ "and I only bought it today!"

"If we don't leave now, ☐ said Mum angrily, "we'll miss the plane! ☐

---

3 Punctuate this passage with inverted commas, full stops and commas.

I don't want to go out because it's too hot said Grandad

We need honey for this recipe said Amir and we have none

Go and ask Lily said Paul if we have any more ketchup

Lucy is a great artist said Chloe but I'm better at sports

4 Each sentence below has one punctuation mistake. Write out the sentences again so that they are punctuated correctly.

"I play football on Mondays." said Luke, "and on Fridays."

....

"I like mint ice cream, said Milly, "and vanilla."

....

"Do you know," asked Simon, "where we are"?

....

"They're coming" said the captain, "so hide the treasure!"

....

5 Use the words in the boxes to write a sentence that includes inverted commas.

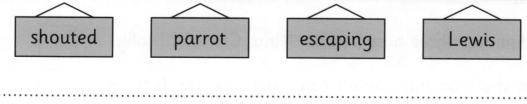

....

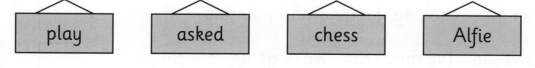

....

"I can punctuate speech correctly."

Colons

Colons can be used to introduce a list or an explanation.

> Our playground has lots of things: a slide, a roundabout and swings.

In an explanation, the first part is explained by the second part.

> I'm so tired: I didn't sleep last night.

The part before the colon must always be a main clause.

1 These sentences have <u>too many</u> colons.
<u>Cross out</u> the colons which <u>aren't needed</u>.

You need several things for the trip: a rucksack, a clipboard: and some paper.

I've forgotten my house: keys: I left in such a rush: this morning.

The fire procedure is simple: sound the alarm, leave: calmly: and call 999.

I can't: possibly eat this: it's got mushrooms: in it.

I don't think this house is suitable: there's a huge hole: in the roof.

My brother has three jobs: painter, removal: man: and waiter.

I am going to build: a rocket this weekend: I want to go: to space.

2 <u>Tick</u> the <u>sentences</u> which use colons <u>correctly</u>.

Nadine has three best friends: Nina, Cat and Molly. ☐

I am stuck on this game I can't: get past the first level. ☐

Mum likes: cooking, jogging and painting. ☐

I can't wait for tomorrow: we're going to a museum. ☐

I can speak three languages: French, Italian and Thai. ☐

Mr Blake is feeling miserable he's hurt: his back. ☐

> The part before the colon must be a main clause.

3 **Add** the **colons** in the **correct places** in these sentences.

Dad has loads of tools in his shed saws, spanners and hammers.

The crew feared Captain Rogers he had never lost a sword fight.

Enzo was crying in the kitchen he had burnt the dinner again.

I have a short Christmas list a board game, a jumper and a puppy.

Sabrina has very unusual pets two spiders, a snake and a hedgehog.

Pancakes have three main ingredients eggs, milk and flour.

I'm going to wear two pairs of tights today it's freezing outside.

I'm expecting three packages a phone cover, a skirt and some boots.

Rob doesn't like going outside at night he's afraid of bats.

4 Choose **three items** from the **box** to complete **each list** using a **colon**.

bread   cakes   pastries   ladybirds   hockey   bees
tennis   netball   crickets

Our bakery sells lots of things...

I have three favourite insects ....

I play three sports ....

5 **Write a sentence** about the **picture** below which includes a **colon**.

....

....

"I can use colons to introduce lists and explanations."

Section 6 — Colons and Semi-Colons

Semi-Colons

Semi-colons **can separate** long phrases or clauses **in a list.**
This is usually when there are other punctuation **marks in the items.**

> At the vets I saw three tiny, ginger cats; two dogs, both with broken legs; and a long-haired rabbit.

Unlike with commas, you need a semi-colon before the last item.

Semi-colons **can also** join two clauses **in a sentence instead of a conjunction.**
They both have to be main clauses, equally important **and** about the same thing.

> Jake hated the film; Helena thought it was brilliant.

1 **Write out** the **pairs** of main clauses with a **semi-colon** and a **full stop.**

I got a new bike   my brother got a car

....

My dad is English   my mum is German

....

I love ballet   my cousin loves tap

....

2 **Tick** the **sentences** where a **semi-colon** could be used **instead** of the **conjunction.**

Find a place to hide <u>or</u> you'll be in trouble. ☐

The robber grabbed his bag <u>and</u> ran away. ☐

I was absolutely starving <u>so</u> ate the lot. ☐

I couldn't believe it <u>but</u> I had come last. ☐

3 Add the missing semi-colons to these lists.

Jonas had Geography, where they were taking samples in the field History, his favourite by far and then English with Mr Jeffries.

The trapeze artists flew through the air, effortlessly and skilfully the magicians, my favourite, made all sorts of things vanish and the three fire-breathers were truly breathtaking!

The flight was late, delayed by three hours the seats were uncomfortable, especially mine and the in-flight food was horrid.

Ice skating is difficult: it hurts when you fall over, which happens a lot you have to be careful with the blades on your boots and you have to avoid others on the ice, which can be tricky!

4 Finish the sentence using the words in boxes and semi-colons.

then she spread the mixture into a baking tin

first she mixed all the ingredients together

then she baked it for twenty minutes.

Gemma baked a cake: ....

....

....

....

"I can break up lists and sentences with semi-colons."

Section 6 — Colons and Semi-Colons

Colons and Semi-Colons

Remember, colons introduce lists and explanations, and semi-colons break up lists and clauses in a sentence. Punctuation can change the meaning:

I sleep all day; I work all night   I sleep all day: I work all night

A semi-colon means that these two parts are related and equally important, but they're separate.

With a colon, the second part explains the first part, so this means I sleep all day because I work all night.

1 Write out the words and punctuation in the crates into full sentences.

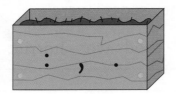
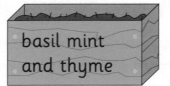
basil mint and thyme
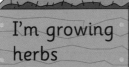
I'm growing herbs

....

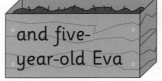
and five-year-old Eva
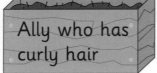
Ally who has curly hair
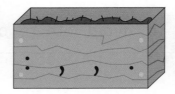
I have two sisters

....

....

2 Complete each sentence with either a colon or a semi-colon.

I ate all my vegetables ..... carrots, peas and broccoli.

We need to clean the house ..... the Queen is coming.

London is a capital city ..... Ulverston is a small town.

We have three ducks ..... Beatrice, Eugene and Nigel.

Grasshoppers have six legs ..... spiders have eight legs.

3 | **Write out** the **sentences**, replacing the **conjunction** with a **colon** or a **semi-colon**.

Kim stayed outside <u>because</u> Gran had come round.

....

On Monday I bake <u>and</u> on Tuesday I sew.

....

Ali groomed her dog <u>as</u> the pageant was tomorrow.

....

Harry is a painter <u>whilst</u> Yuri is a teacher.

....

I can make pasta, <u>but</u> I can't make pancakes.

....

Nico screamed <u>because</u> the room was on fire!

....

4 | **Punctuate** these passages with **colons** and **semi-colons**.

Everyone had helped with the show Mrs Dastur had painted the sets, one for every scene all the children, even the reception class, had made props and the mayor had let them use the village hall.

The explorer told an exciting tale he had waded across rivers, fighting crocodiles in his path slept in trees, without a hammock, with the monkeys and examined all sorts of wonderful insects.

"I can use colons and semi-colons correctly."

Section 6 — Colons and Semi-Colons

Paragraphs

Paragraphs are used to show when a new subject, place or time are introduced. You also need to start a new paragraph when a new person speaks.

(1) Group these sentences into paragraphs.
Put the letters of the sentences in the boxes.

a) I live in a small village.

b) I go to my school by bus.

c) My house has a red door.

d) It has a bakery and a bank.

e) School starts at 8.45 am.

f) 200 people live in my village.

g) My school is in Biglinton.

h) It has a big kitchen and living room.

i) I share a bedroom with my sister.

j) There is a park in the town centre.

k) The lessons finish at 3.30 pm.

l) There's a garden behind the house.

Paragraph 1: [a] [ ] [ ] [ ]

Paragraph 2: [c] [ ] [ ] [ ]

Paragraph 3: [g] [ ] [ ] [ ]

(2) Put paragraph markers (//) into this passage
to show where new paragraphs should start.

"Come over here, Ellie," called Grandad, looking up from his potato planting. "What is it?" I asked, wading over to him through the mud and bags of freshly picked vegetables. "I want you to learn how to plant seeds," he told me. "Fine," I replied. I stood and watched obediently, trying to concentrate on Grandad and ignore the worms wriggling at my feet. "Now, let's see if you've got my magic touch," he smiled, handing me the bag.

"I can use paragraphs to break up my writing."

Layout Devices

There are lots of different layout devices that help to make the presentation of informative writing more interesting:

headings   subheadings   columns   bullet points   boxes   tables

1 Label the different layout features in the leaflet below.

① **BAKINGTON SAFARI PARK**

Go on Safari ②

See our animal friends:
- elephants
- rhinos
- lions
- zebras

Food

Try one of our tasty dishes:
- Jungle cereal ④
- Beasty burgers
- Fierce fry-up
- Safari salad

⑤ New petting zoo for 2014!

Feed the Animals

Penguins	11:00
Otters	12:30
Meerkats	2:00
Monkeys	3:15

③

Contact Us

For more information
telephone: 05796 666444
or email: bookings@bakington.pps

1: ....

2: ....

3: ....

4: ....

5: ....

"I understand how layout features work in a text."

Writing Lists

You can use numbered points or bullet points to write a list.
Always introduce a list with a colon.

Items usually
follow the
same word
pattern

My room has:
• a bed
• a desk
• a wardrobe

To cook from frozen:
1) heat oven to 180 °C
2) remove film lid
3) cook for 20 mins

You only need
to use capital
letters or full
stops if the
items are full
sentences.

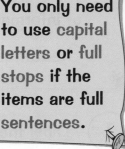

1 **Write** out this passage as a **list** of **numbered points**.

Mix the dry ingredients together. Whisk the eggs with the

milk. Add the liquid to the dry ingredients. Spread the

mixture into baking tins. Bake at 180 °C for twelve minutes.

1) ....

2) ....

3) ....

4) ....

5) ....

2 **Write a list** of four things you could do this weekend using **bullet points**.

This weekend I could: ....

....

....

....

"I can organise information into lists."

PSHE and Citizenship

Key Stage 2

Judy Hunter and Sheila Phillips

Contents

Introduction

This resource

This resource is designed to cover the requirements of the curricula of England, Wales, Scotland and Northern Ireland. Charts matching the contents of this resource can be found on pages x–xix.

Activities within this resource are based on the belief that to make healthier choices, to develop respect, to play an active role as citizens, to act responsibly, children need more than information alone. They need the skills to use the information they learn and the self-esteem/sense of self-worth to put what they might know into practice.

'The child must first learn self-respect and a sense of dignity that grows out of his increasing self-understanding before he can learn to respect the personalities and rights and differences of others.'

(Virginia M. Axline *In Search of Self*)

Whist this resource focuses particularly on the 'content' of the PSHE and citizenship curriculum, activities are designed to enable pupils to develop skills by working together, discussing together and valuing the opinions and ideas of others. We recommend that activities are interspersed with further skill development and self-esteem raising activities, through circle work for example (see 'Teaching and learning styles' on page iv).

An emphasis on skill development and raising self-esteem at Key Stages 1 and 2 lays the foundation for the more detailed information which follows at Key Stages 3 and 4 – it puts the building blocks in place:

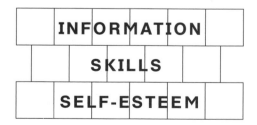

The cement which holds the blocks together is the opportunity for children to see a model for PSHE and citizenship within their lives – to live it, to reflect upon it and to learn from it. School councils and forums are one example.

' ... over time, a continuing and steadfast focus on the positive in life, on our strengths, and on the strengths of others can help to restore in our students their personal energy, their feeling of power, their sense of worth so they can see themselves as positive forces who can contribute to the task of building a better world.'

(Robert C. Hawley *Human Values in the Classroom*)

Topics/aspects of PSHE and citizenship need to be revisited through a spiral curriculum approach, that is a planned curriculum which reviews, consolidates and extends children's understanding and skills and allows them to assimilate knowledge when it is appropriate to their age, their maturity and their ability. It is therefore important to collaborate with Key Stage 1 teachers to determine what has gone before, and equally important to collaborate with Key Stage 3 teachers to consider what comes next. This is just one of the issues that primary and secondary schools will need to incorporate into their transition programmes for pupils.

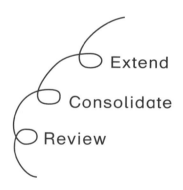

The notion of a spiral curriculum demands that we also take the time to review what children know and understand and what their perceptions are, otherwise many of the messages we are trying to impart, many of the skills we are trying to develop are lost. Children can see the world very differently to adults. The Draw and Write technique developed by Noreen M. Wetton (The Health Education Unit at the University of Southampton) is an excellent technique for establishing children's perceptions and we strongly recommend it to you.

This model of delivery fits comfortably with the overall goal for citizenship as documented in Education for Citizenship in Scotland:

'Education for citizenship should aim to develop capacity for thoughtful and responsible participation in political, economic, social and cultural life. This capacity is rooted in knowledge and understanding, in a range of generic skills and competencies, including 'core skills', and in a variety of personal qualities and dispositions. It finds expression through creative and enterprising approaches to issues and problems.

Being a capable citizen is not just about possessing knowledge and skills. It is about being able and willing to use knowledge and skills to take decisions and act. Nor is effective citizenship just about having the capacity and disposition to be active. It is about being able to take action and make things happen for ends – and by means – that are infused with respect and care for people and a sense of social and environmental responsibility.

Finally, capability for citizenship, as envisaged here, includes ideas about 'political literacy'. It also encompasses social, economic and cultural 'literacies' coupled with the capacity for participation in all aspects of society – political, economic, social and cultural.'

The Framework for PSHE and citizenship at Key Stages 1 and 2, as published in *The National Curriculum Handbook* for primary teachers in England (1999), states that pupils should gain the *knowledge*, *skills* and *understanding* to:

1   develop confidence and responsibility and make the most of their abilities.
2   prepare to play an active role as citizens.
3   develop a healthy, safer lifestyle.
4   develop good relationships and respect the differences between people.

A whole school approach

Whilst this resource focuses on topics/aspects which are specific to PSHE and citizenship, it is not intended to be seen or used in isolation from other opportunities that form a whole school approach. PSHE and citizenship is a way of 'being' with children, it is a modelling of the relationships and behaviours we are seeking to develop in them, it is a way of bringing the learning to life, it is about respecting children and involving them in their learning. The activities chosen as a focus for specific work are important, and so are the processes happening within the classroom and within the whole school environment. PSHE and citizenship is about maximising planned learning opportunities through the curriculum as a whole.

The need to 'model' and 'bring alive' citizenship is summed up by the following:

'Education for citizenship is more than a simple expectation of political literacy. Civics lessons are not enough. The ethos of the school must be conducive to good citizenship.'

(Douglas, Osler, *Education for Citizenship in the New Scotland*, Gordon Cook Foundation, 1999)

Similarly, the Welsh *Personal and Social Education Framework* states:

'A whole school approach to PSE will incorporate a range of experiences to promote the personal and social well-being of children and young people and enable them to develop a sense of self-worth and relate effectively to others. PSE will equip them to be more informed, confident and skilled in order to take an active and responsible part in society and it will enhance learning, motivation, performance and achievement.'

The National Healthy School Standard (NHSS) was launched in October 1999 and is jointly supported by the Department for Education and Skills (DfES) and the Department of Health (DH). It advocates a whole school approach, focuses on school improvement issues and supports schools in the development of PSHE and citizenship.

Teaching and learning styles

A range of teaching strategies need to be used to provide all children with learning opportunities and we have endeavoured to offer a range within this resource. PSHE and citizenship does, however, lend itself particularly to active learning, discussion work, enquiry and participation in 'real life' projects and teachers will be able to extend material to take this into account. Many messages can be reinforced through assembly work.

Circle work is an excellent methodology for building a classroom environment where pupils can develop skills and self-esteem and many teachers will be familiar with its processes and structure. In facilitating the process of children developing their own ground rules, understanding the importance of equality in the circle, learning to listen and take turns, negotiate issues and reach consensus on decision making, teachers are providing a model of PSHE and citizenship 'in action'. Additional information on circle work is shown on page ix.

Outside agencies and visitors can enhance programmes and complement the work of teachers. However, attention needs to be given to how a school ensures that visitors' values and philosophies are compatible with those of the school. Time needs to be spent planning together and reviewing together.

Involving parents/carers

Effectively involving parents/carers in the education of their children can be a difficult task and yet they are often the greatest influence in a child's life. A school's task is to educate the citizens, the workforce, the parents of tomorrow and to do that they may well need to also educate the parents of today. Involving parents/carers in PSHE and citizenship education can have two functions: it can enhance children's educational experiences, and it can also be a means of educating their parents/carers. Where appropriate we have suggested ways of involving parents/carers through some of the pupil activities.

Assessment, recording and reporting

Children (and their parents/carers) have the same right to know how they are progressing in PSHE and citizenship as they do for any other aspect of the curriculum. Self-reflection/assessment and the ability to begin to set targets for themselves are an important part of a child's development and should be seen as an integral part of the PSHE and citizenship programme. In the *PSHE and citizenship Framework* we are given two broad areas for assessment:

- Children's knowledge and understanding, for example information on health, understanding of rules, understanding of health and safety procedures, and the meaning of ideas, including democracy.
- How well children can use their knowledge and understanding in developing skills and attitudes, for example through participating in discussions, group tasks and activities, managing conflict, making decisions and promoting positive relationships.

Within the framework we are also told:

'Assessment in PSHE and citizenship should not imply that children are failing as people or citizens. It should not be a judgement on the worth, personality or value of an individual child or their family. This can be particularly important to working with children from diverse backgrounds or who have emotional and behavioural difficulties. A record of children's progress and portfolios of work will provide evidence for reports to parents that might include their child's awareness of topical events, exercise of responsibility and contribution to the life of the school.

Schools may wish to recognise children's achievements in PSHE and citizenship by awarding their own certificates. These could be linked with a school's system of commendations.'

In looking at your PSHE and citizenship curriculum, in conjunction with other curriculum areas, the learning outcomes for Key Stage 2, as detailed in *Passport: A framework for personal and social development*, commissioned by the Calouste Gulbenkian Foundation can prove a useful tool. Copies of the document can be obtained by calling 020 7636 5313.

Themes/Aspects

We have incorporated the *aspects* or *themes* of the Frameworks/Guidelines for England, Wales, Scotland and Northern Ireland and have divided this resource into activities which cover the following:

- Growing and changing
- Medicines and drugs
- Keeper safer
- Feelings and feeling good
- Friendships, families and being me
- Looking good and keeping well
- The environment
- Citizenship
- Moving on
- Reviewing progress

How to use this book

Both the teacher's notes and the activity sheets are intended to be used with the minimum of preparation and additional resources. The activity sheets are photocopiable. The length of lessons/activities may vary as we realise schools will have differing amounts of time to devote to PSHE and citizenship and will choose to deliver their programmes in different ways.

Above all, we hope you enjoy working with your children in the delivery of PSHE and citizenship.

Using children's literature to develop PSHE and citizenship

Literature can provide an excellent means of exploring some of the issues that children often find difficult to talk about and for developing a language which enables children to express their emotions. They struggle to find words to describe frustration, isolation, empathy, joy ... yet their feelings are as complex as any adult's. Through literature we can take children into situations that we would not, and could not, take them to in reality. They can face dangers, be afraid with, and for, the characters, be surprised, angry, joyful – experience a whole range of human emotions.

Children can be encouraged to discuss issues (often seen as 'sensitive' issues) through the characters; this can be more comfortable for them than talking about themselves directly. They are able to explore the experiences and emotions of the characters. As the children become more confident and develop an emotional language, they will begin to talk more freely about their own thoughts and feelings. They can consider the behaviour of the characters, and the situations in which the characters find themselves. They can get inside the characters' problems and decide how they would respond and what options they would choose. Children's literature therefore provides us with multiple opportunities, not only for literacy development but also for engaging the children in PSHE and citizenship issues.

You will have a wide range of books in school already. Look at them from a different perspective and you will readily see how they can be used. Don't be afraid of using books that may seem too young for Key Stage 2 pupils. There is a huge range of picture story books that put across the key messages you are trying to convey, and that can be read with the class in just a few minutes. With older children's books, look for a particular chapter or extract that will stimulate discussion and then make the book available for children wishing to read more. Remember to include some poetry in your collection.

Here are some useful books you probably have on the shelf already. The list is not exclusive or exhaustive, it is simply intended to stimulate some ideas and get you started. It is difficult to place books into categories of themes as they can cover so many different issues within just one story. Use the children as your resource – they will have many ideas of what issues are contained within a book so be led by them and their imaginations.

Theme: Growing and changing

Penguin's Progress by Jill Tomlinson
Mammoth Books 0-7497-0867-0

Otto is a penguin chick, but he is different from all the other chicks he knows. He is 'first chick', the first penguin born that year, so it's his job to look after all the younger ones as they grow up. But nobody has told him what 'growing up' means, and life is both confusing and exciting.

Once There Were Giants by Martin Waddell
Walker Books Ltd.
0-7445-1791-5

Once there was a baby in the house, and to that baby, Mum, Dad, Jill, John, and Uncle Tom were giants. But, little by little, the baby changes, grows and develops in many ways until she becomes a giant too. A story of the family cycle.

The Gorilla Who Wanted To Grow Up by Jill Tomlinson
Mammoth Books
0-7497-0865-4

Pongo is a young gorilla who can't wait to grow up, so that he can have a silver back like his father's and a big chest that he can thump! First, though, Pongo has to learn how grown-up gorillas survive in the jungle.

Mummy Laid an Egg by Babette Cole
Red Fox 0-09-929911-9

Mum and Dad decide it's time they told the children about the facts of life. Mum says that babies are made out of gingerbread, grown from seeds in the greenhouse, or squidged out of tubes. Dad says that Mummy laid an egg with the two children inside. So it's up to the children to put them right on a few things ...

Ramona Forever by Beverley Cleary
Puffin 0-14-031916-6

The arrival of Howie Kemp's rich Uncle Hobart from Saudi Arabia heralds a sequence of unexpected events in the Quimby household. For Ramona, there are exciting times like being a bridesmaid; worrying times like maybe having to move if Mr Quimby gets a new job; and sad times like when Picky-Picky dies. But Ramona survives all these ups and downs, proving that she is winning at growing up and that she is still the same old wonderful, blunderful Ramona.

Theme: Friendships, families and being me

Nothing by Mick Inkpen, Hodder Children's Books 0-340-64650-0

A little creature lives in the attic, alone and forgotten. It cannot even remember its own name. One day the attic door is flung open ... and so begins Nothing's search to discover who he really is.

Amazing Grace by Mary Hoffman
Frances Lincoln Ltd
0-7112-0699-6

Grace, with the support of her mother and grandmother, discovers that you can do anything you want to, as long as you set your mind to it.

Little Beaver And The Echo by Amy MacDonald
Walker Books Ltd
0-7445-0443-0

Little Beaver lives all alone by the edge of the pond. He doesn't have any brothers. He doesn't have any sisters. Worst of all, he doesn't have any friends. One day, when he starts to cry, he hears someone else crying too, on the other side of his pond ... And so begins his touching quest for a friend.

The Suitcase Kid by Jacqueline Wilson
Transworld Publishers
0-440-86311-2

Ten-year old Andy shares her experience of life after divorce in a realistic, but often very funny, story. 'My family lived at Mulberry Cottage. Mum, Dad, me – and Radish, my Sylvanian rabbit. But now Mum lives with Bill the Baboon and his three kids. Dad lives with Carrier and her twins. And where do I live? I live out of a suitcase. One week with Mum's new family and one week with Dad's.'

'I Wanna Be Your Mate' from *Poems about Friends* selected by Tony Bradman
Bloomsbury Children's Books
0-7475-4451-4

Sometimes friends can be there when you need them – and sometimes they can be a real pain ... in fact, some friends are perfect for getting you out of trouble – and others are perfect for getting you right back in again.

Theme: Feelings and feeling good

Red Sky In The Morning by Elizabeth Laird
Macmillan Children's Books
0-434-94714-8

Anna is a young teenager whose parents are having a baby quite late in their lives. Anna is looking forward to the baby coming and she thinks it will give her a chance to show all the family how grown up she is. Ben is born with hydrocephalus and Anna finds herself full of love for him and teaches him things a step at a time. She wants her school friends and strangers to know that her brother is beautiful, funny and clever in his own special way, but finds this is very difficult.

Secret Friends by Elizabeth Laird
Hodder Books 0-340-66473-8

'It's crazy, starting at a new school. For days you feel so new and lost it's as if you've wandered into a foreign country where you can't speak the language.' Rafaella doesn't find it easy to make friends. Her name sounds strange. Her ears stick out. She feels different from the others.

Fun Is A Feeling by Chara M. Curtis
Illumination Arts
0-935699-13-9

This inspiring story encourages us to discover the fun hidden in many of life's experiences – and to treasure each of our feelings. A child finds that the joy of life begins from within.

Badger's Parting Gifts by Susan Varley
Picture Lions 0-00-664317-5

When old Badger dies, his friends think they will be sad forever. But gradually they are able to remember Badger with joy and to treasure the gifts he left behind for every one of his friends. A sensitive book than can help children come to terms with the death of those they love.

I'll Always Love You by Hans Wilhelm
Hodder Children's Books
0-340-40153-2

The story of a boy and his best friend. All the family love Elfie, but the boy knows she's his dog. They do everything together. As the boy grows taller, Elfie gets rounder and slower, until one day she's not there any more. The young boy faces the loss of his companion but remembers what he always told her: 'I'll always love you'.

Theme: Citizenship

The True Story Of The Three Little Pigs by Jon Scieszka
Penguin Books 0-14-054056-3

You may think you know the story of the three little pigs and the big bad wolf – but are you sure you know the real story? This is the story as told by A. Wolf who tells his tale and his feelings.

Two Monsters by David McKee
Random House 0-09-945530-7

Reconciling differences. Two monsters, who both think they are absolutely 'right', come to understand that they can both be right, but they destroy the mountain in the process.

What If The Zebras Lost Their Stripes? by John Reitano
Paulist Press 0-8091-6649-6

A story that teaches children respect for individual differences. A story that confronts us with the absurdity of racism and prejudice based on skin colour.

Angus Rides The Goods Train by Alan Durant
Penguin Books 0-670-86924-4

When the goods train, laden with milk and honey and rice, speeds away across land and sea, Angus is full of excitement as he stands beside the driver. But why won't the train stop for those who are hungry and thirsty? What can Angus do?

Journey to Jo'burg A South African Story by Beverley Naidoo
Longman Group Ltd
0-00-672693-3

Frightened their baby sister Dineo will die, thirteen-year-old Naledi and her younger brother Tiro run away from their grandmother to Johannesburg to find their mother, who works there as a maid. Their journey illustrates at every turn the grim realities of apartheid – the pass laws, bantustans, racism, the breakdown of family life. The opulence of white 'Madam's' house contrasts starkly with their reality – their baby sister is suffering from starvation, not an incurable disease.

AND MANY, MANY MORE!!

You may also find *Hand In Hand, Emotional Development Through Literature* (Saffire Press 1-901564-03-7) a helpful resource. This was written by the authors of this book in conjunction with Noreen Wetton.

Circle work for the development of PSHE and citizenship

Those who know the value of working in this way with the children, know it is an excellent vehicle for development of skill and raising self-esteem.

If the circle is the safe place it is meant to be, the children can also learn about themselves and their interactions with others. It can be a place where 'I am valued for being me – with all my qualities and peculiarities and a place where I can try some new behaviour with everyone's support'. Central to this aim is the equality of those in the circle. Everyone, adult, child, those good at maths and those slow to learn, are all equally valued and have a say in making the rules.

This may be a child's first experience of being involved in a negotiation of what rules will apply in this situation and to have a shared responsibility for the upkeep of those rules. This is not a place where someone else's rule gets imposed but a place where our rules, which we made together, are supported by us all.

If the circle is a place where children can develop trust in each other and take risks with leaving behind old ways of doing things, then new skills can be learned and new confidence to 'be me' found.

'Trust is the result of a risk successfully survived.'

(Jack R. Gibb)

Many children fall into behaviours around health choices because it is safer to go with the crowd than to take a risk and have the confidence to stand out from the crowd. If our children can value their uniqueness they can make healthy choices for themselves.

'A survey of college students showed that 90% were dissatisfied in some way with their appearance. If the words 'normal' or 'average' mean anything at all, it is obvious that 90% of our population, cannot be 'abnormal' or 'different' or 'defective' in appearance. Yet similar surveys have shown that approximately the same percentage of the general population find some reason to be ashamed of their body image.'

(Maxwell Maltz from *Psycho-Cybernetics*)

Circle time is an opportunity to value all individuals equally – their ideas, bodies, intellectual capacity and individuality. If the child experiences this value and accepts herself as she is, maybe her energy can go into being an individual in a society rather than inwardly wishing she were different.

The claims for the effect of circle work on a child's confidence and a class's relationships may seem extreme. We can only invite you to get a good book and give it a try for yourself. The two most common responses we hear from teachers trying to work in this way are:

'I didn't think the children were capable of behaving in such a way.' And,

'I haven't enjoyed being with my class so much for a long time.'

England Curriculum Guidelines

Knowledge, skills and understanding

Developing confidence and responsibility and making the most of their abilities

		Key Blueprints Units
1	Pupils should be taught:	
a	to talk and write about their opinions, and explain their views, on issues that affect themselves and society	15, 16, 19, 24, 35, 41
b	to recognise their worth as individuals by identifying positive things about themselves and their achievements, seeing their mistakes, making amends and setting personal goals	16, 17, 19, 23, 24, 41
c	to face new challenges positively by collecting information, looking for help, making responsible choices, and taking action	11, 32, 41
d	to recognise, as they approach puberty, how people's emotions change at that time and how to deal with their feelings towards themselves, their family and others in a positive way	2, 4
e	about the range of jobs carried out by people they know, and to understand how they can develop skills to make their own contribution in the future	39
f	to look after their money and realise that future wants and needs may be met through saving.	34, 39

Preparing to play an active role as citizens

2	Pupils should be taught:	
a	to research, discuss and debate topical issues, problems and events	
b	why and how rules and laws are made and enforced, why different rules are needed in different situations and how to take part in making and changing rules	31, 32, 35
c	to realise the consequences of anti-social and aggressive behaviours, such as bullying and racism, on individuals and communities	18, 34, 40
d	that there are different kinds of responsibilities, rights and duties at home, at school and in the community, and that these can sometimes conflict with each other	18, 21, 22, 23, 25, 31, 34, 35, 36, 37
e	to reflect on spiritual, moral, social, and cultural issues, using imagination to understand other people's experiences	20, 22, 36, 37, 40

f	to resolve differences by looking at alternatives, making decisions and explaining choices	23
g	what democracy is, and about the basic institutions that support it locally and nationally	33, 34
h	to recognise the role of voluntary, community and pressure groups	33, 36
i	to appreciate the range of national, regional, religious and ethnic identities in the United Kingdom	22, 36, 37
j	that resources can be allocated in different ways and that these economic choices affect individuals, communities and the sustainability of the environment	31, 32, 33
k	to explore how the media present information.	9, 38

Developing a healthy, safer lifestyle

3	Pupils should be taught:	
a	what makes a healthy lifestyle, including the benefits of exercise and healthy eating, what affects mental health, and how to make informed choices	26, 27, 28
b	that bacteria and viruses can affect health and that following simple, safe routines can reduce their spread	29
c	about how the body changes as they approach puberty	1, 5
d	which commonly available substances and drugs are legal and illegal, their effects and risks	6, 7, 8, 9, 10
e	to recognise the different risks in different situations and then decide how to behave responsibly, including sensible road use, and judging what kind of physical contact is acceptable or unacceptable	8, 10, 11, 12, 13, 14, 15
f	that pressure to behave in an unacceptable or risky way can come from a variety of sources, including people they know, and how to ask for help and use basic techniques for resisting pressure to do wrong	8, 9, 10, 13, 23, 30
g	school rules about health and safety, basic emergency aid procedures and where to get help.	10, 13, 30

Developing good relationships and respecting the differences between people

4 Pupils should be taught:

a	that their actions affect themselves and others, to care about other people's feelings and to try to see things from their points of view	12, 18, 20, 21
b	to think about the lives of people living in other places and times, and people with different values and customs	22
c	to be aware of different types of relationship, including marriage and those between friends and families, and to develop the skills to be effective in relationships	4, 21, 25
d	to realise the nature and consequences of racism, teasing, bullying and aggressive behaviours, and how to respond to them and ask for help	9, 18
e	to recognise and challenge stereotypes	9
f	that differences and similarities between people arise from a number of factors, including cultural, ethnic, racial and religious diversity, gender and disability	22
g	where individuals, families and groups can get help and support.	13, 30

Breadth of opportunities

5 During the key stage, pupils should be taught the **knowledge, skills and understanding** through opportunities to:

a	take responsibility (for example, for planning and looking after the school environment; for the needs of others, such as by acting as a peer supporter, as a befriender, or as a playground mediator for younger pupils; for looking after animals properly; for identifying safe, healthy and sustainable means of travel when planning their journey to school)	8, 18, 23, 26
b	feel positive about themselves (for example, by producing personal diaries, profiles and portfolios of achievements; by having opportunities to show what they can do and how much responsibility they can take)	4, 17, 19, 24
c	participate (for example, in the school's decision-making process, relating it to democratic structures and processes such as councils, parliaments, government and voting)	11, 31, 33, 34

d	make real choices and decisions (for example, about issues affecting their health and well-being such as smoking; on the use of scarce resources; how to spend money, including pocket money and contributions to charities)	7, 12, 31, 32, 34
e	meet and talk with people (for example, people who contribute to society through environmental pressure groups or international aid organisations; people who work in the school and the neighbourhood, such as religious leaders, community police officers)	14, 31, 35, 37
f	develop relationships through work and play (for example, taking part in activities with groups that have particular needs, such as children with special needs and the elderly; communicating with children in other countries by satellite, e-mail or letters)	18, 36
g	consider social and moral dilemmas that they come across in life (for example, encouraging respect and understanding between different races and dealing with harassment)	37
h	find information and advice (for example, through helplines; by understanding about welfare systems in society)	1, 7, 14, 30
i	prepare for change (for example, transferring to secondary school).	41

Scotland – Health Education 5–14 National Guidelines

Key Stage 2 match to *Blueprints PSHE and Citizenship*

Strand	Level C	Level D
Physical health This strand explores physical factors in relation to our health and looking after ourselves	• Show their knowledge and understanding of what they do to keep healthy, e.g. effect of regular exercise, leisure activities, choosing nutritious food **26, 27, 28**	• Show their knowledge and physical needs and strengths
	• Identify ways of reducing risks of infection, e.g. oral hygiene **29**	• Show their knowledge of how the body is protected from infection, e.g. natural immunity, vaccinations **29**
	• Show their knowledge and understanding of the impact of harmful substances on the body **7, 8**	• Identify strategies for keeping healthy and safe, e.g. choosing not to use harmful substances **6, 8, 9**
	• Demonstrate simple decision-making strategies in relation to keeping healthy and safe **9, 11, 12, 13, 15**	• Show knowledge and understanding of their own body's uniqueness **24**
	• Identify the different ways in which people grow and change, e.g. in puberty **1, 5**	• Show their knowledge and understanding of their own developing sexuality **2, 4**
Emotional health This strand explores emotions, feelings and relationships and how they affect our mental well-being	• Use personal and interpersonal skills to relate to other people **21, 40** KS1 unit 38	• Demonstrate an understanding of their emotional needs and strengths, e.g. resilience and ways of managing pressure **8, 16, 17, 24, 25, 28**

- Recognise the ways in which behaviour can influence people's relationships
  18, 23

- Show ways in which they can deal with change, e.g. transition from primary to secondary school
  41

- Recognise the link between body image, self-worth and external influences

- Recognise that peer and media influences can affect choices they make
  9, 23, 38

- Recognise issues of discrimination and the right to equal opportunity for all members of the community
  32, 34, 36

- Show ways of making and keeping friends, e.g. playing together
  21

- Recognise how circumstances can change emotions, e.g. moving house or changing school
  25

- Identify strategies to help deal with loss and grief
  20
  KS1 unit 23

- Show safe ways of dealing with a range of situations, particularly those that may present risk, e.g. bullying
  9, 12, 13, 40
  KS1 unit 34

Social health
This strand explores the interaction of the individual, the community and the environment in relation to health and safety

- Demonstrate safe ways of responding to risks to health and personal safety in their community, e.g. following codes of safety
  8, 9, 11, 13, 14, 30

- Identify a range of ways of travelling safely
  14, 15

- Show an understanding of how they can contribute responsibly to their community, e.g. avoiding creating litter
  31
  KS1 units 33, 37, 39, 40

Wales Curriculum Guidelines

KS2 Personal and Social Education Framework

Pupils should:	Key Blueprints Units
Social aspect	
Recognise and understand the power of peer influence and pressure	8, 40
Understand the benefits of friends and families and the challenges and issues that can arise	19, 21, 22, 23, 25
Understand the nature of bullying, including sexual harassment, and the harm that can result	13, 40
Community aspect	
Know about aspects of their cultural heritage in Wales, including the multi-cultural dimension	22, 36, 37
Understand the importance of democratic decision-making and involvement and how injustice and inequality affect people's lives	31, 32, 33, 34, 35
Physical aspect	
Know about the harmful effects, both to themselves and others, of tobacco, alcohol, solvents and other legal and illegal substances	6, 7, 8, 9, 10
Understand the benefits of exercise and hygiene and the need for a variety of food for growth and activity	26, 27, 28, 29
Recognise how to be safe at home, on the road, near water, and in the sun	10, 11, 12, 14, 15
Know what to do or to whom to go when feeling unsafe	10, 11, 13, 30
Sexual aspect	
Understand the physical and emotional changes which take place at puberty	1, 4, 5
Know how babies are conceived	3
Understand how the baby develops in the uterus and is born	3
Emotional aspect	
Know and understand the range of their own and others' feelings and emotions	17, 18, 25, 40
Understand the changes in feelings at times of change and loss	20, 41
Understand the situations which produce conflict	25

Aspect		Pages
Spiritual aspect	Recognise the uniqueness and independence of individuals	19, 23, 24
	Understand that people have different beliefs which shape the way they live	36
	Acknowledge that there are mysteries in life and death	
Moral aspect	Understand that their actions have consequences	12, 18, 35
	Know that people differ in what they believe is right and wrong	35, 37
Vocational aspect	Know about the process and people involved in the production, distribution and selling of goods and the role of advertising from the local to the global level	38, 39
	Understand the limitations on and costs and benefits of spending choices	39
Learning aspect	Identify strengths and weaknesses and set targets for improvement	41
	Know the ways in which they learn best	
Environmental aspect	Know how the environment can be affected by human activity	31, 32
	Understand how conflict can arise from different views about environmental issues	32, 33

Northern Ireland Curriculum Guidelines

Guidance for Primary Schools: Relationships and Sexuality Education	Key Blueprints Units
Myself	
• My body, how it works and how to keep it healthy	6, 7, 26, 27, 29
• The physical, social and emotional changes which occur during puberty (girls and boys)	1, 4, 5
• Myself and my peers – different rates of growth and physical development, maturity	4
• Valuing and respecting myself, identifying personal strengths and weaknesses	4, 13, 17, 19, 24
• Feelings, for example, things that make me happy, sad, excited, embarrassed, angry, scared; expressing our feelings, showing love and affection	16, 17, 28
• Gender roles	4
• Making choices – the influences on me and the consequences of actions for oneself and others	8, 12, 18, 23
• Distinguishing between right and wrong	35
• Secrets – knowing the difference between good and bad secrets, what to do about bad secrets	13
• How babies begin and are born; how babies grow; some of the skills necessary for parenting, the importance of good parenting. (Note: decisions on whether or not these topics should be taught to P6/P7 pupils should be agreed in consultation with governors and parents.)	3

My Relationships

• Identifying the positive traits of friendship and their corresponding values	21
• Differences and similarities in people; the need to respect other people's views, emotions and feelings	12, 18, 19, 20, 33
• Families and how they behave – what family members expect of each other	22, 25
• The meaning of friendship and loyalty; making and maintaining friendships and social relationships, for example, identifying and understanding pressures and influences, taking account of other people's point of view	21, 23
• Handling difficult situations, for example, teasing, bullying, death of a family member	20, 40, 41
• The meaning of relationships within families, between friends and in the community.	22, 36
• Behaviour – what constitutes appropriate and non-appropriate physical contact	13
• Identifying dangers and risks within relationships	25
• Being assertive in defending individual rights and beliefs	34
• People who can help pupils when they have anxieties, concerns or questions.	16, 30

My Community/Environment

• Appreciation of the family in relation to the school and the wider community	22, 36
• Cultural differences in families and family relationships	22, 37
• Helping agencies which can support families and individuals in different circumstances	25, 31
• Messages and images about health, gender roles and sexuality from the media, family and peers.	4, 9

QCA Scheme of Work for Citizenship

The QCA Scheme of Work for Citizenship is designed to offer schools flexibility in how they choose to address the aspects of the framework for PSHE and Citizenship for Key Stage 2 that primarily involve citizenship. The following chart suggests the Blueprints units that are most relevant to each unit of the Scheme of Work. Note that the first six Scheme of Work units apply also to Key Stage 1, and matching Blueprints units will be found in Blueprints PSHE & Citizenship Key Stage 1. In the following chart we have suggested three or four Blueprints units for each Scheme of Work unit – two covering the relevant knowledge, skills and understanding, and one or two providing breadth of opportunity.

QCA Scheme of Work unit number and title	PSHE and Citizenship Framework objectives	Blueprints units
1 Taking part – developing skills of communication and participation	Knowledge, skills and understanding 1a, 1c, 1e, 2a, 2b, 2d, 2f, 4a, 1b, 2l	16, 21
	Breadth of opportunity 5a, 5c, 5d, 5e, 5f	1, 4
2 Choices	Knowledge, skills and understanding 1a, 1c, 2a, 2e, 2f, 2j, 3a, 3f	11, 12
	Breadth of opportunity 5c, 5d, 5g	8, 10
3 Animals and us	Knowledge, skills and understanding 2a, 2d, 2h, 2k	9, 25
	Breadth of opportunity 5a, 5c, 5d, 5e, 5h	14, 17
4 People who help us – the local police	Knowledge, skills and understanding 1a, 1e, 2a, 2b, 2d	19, 22
	Breadth of opportunity 5e, 5f, 5g, 5h	30
5 Living in a diverse world	Knowledge, skills and understanding 1a, 1b, 2e, 2i, 4a, 4b, 4e, 4f	15, 24
	Breadth of opportunity 5a, 5b, 5c, 5e, 5f, 5g, 5h	26, 27

Unit	Knowledge, skills and understanding / Breadth of opportunity	Ref.
6 Developing our school grounds	Knowledge, skills and understanding 1a, 2a, 2f, 2j, 3g, 4a	20, 39
	Breadth of opportunity 5a, 5c, 5d, 5e, 5h	48
7 Preparing to play an active role as citizens	Knowledge, skills and understanding 1a, 1b, 2a, 2c, 2d, 2e, 2h, 2i, 4a, 4b, 4d, 4e, 4f	36, 37
	Breadth of opportunity 5a, 5b, 5c, 5d, 5e, 5f, 5g, 5h	13 / 29
8 How do rules and laws affect me?	Knowledge, skills and understanding 1a, 1b, 1c, 2a, 2b, 2c, 2g, 3f, 4a, 4d	33, 35
	Breadth of opportunity 5a, 5b, 5c, 5e, 5g, 5h	42
9 Respect for property	Knowledge, skills and understanding 1a, 2a, 2b, 2c, 2d, 2g, 2j, 4a, 4b	18, 34
	Breadth of opportunity 5a	43
10 Local democracy for young citizens	Knowledge, skills and understanding 1a, 1e, 2a, 2e, 2g, 2k, 4a	31, 40
	Breadth of opportunity 5a, 5b, 5c, 5e, 5f, 5h, 5i	6
11 In the media – what's the news?	Knowledge, skills and understanding 1a, 2a, 2e, 2k, 4b	23, 38
	Breadth of opportunity 5a, 5g, 5h	7
12 Moving on	Knowledge, skills and understanding 1a, 1b, 1c, 1e, 2c, 2f, 4a, 4c, 4d, 4e, 4g	32, 41
	Breadth of opportunity 5a, 5b, 5c	5, 28

Growing and changing

1 Climbing the ladder

Aims
- To develop understanding of the physical changes which begin to occur at puberty.

Teaching points
It is essential to ensure that the learning environment is as safe as possible so that children feel secure and can ask questions and put forward their points of view without fear of ridicule. This applies to all aspects of PSHE and citizenship, and particularly to sex and relationships education. If you have already established ground rules with the class, review them before embarking on these activities. If you have not yet established ground rules, it is advisable to do so – remember they need to be negotiated and not imposed!

Instructions
1   Generate with the children a list of changes that have happened to them since they were born.

2   Discuss which of the changes from the list apply only to girls, which apply only to boys and which apply to both. Emphasise that some changes do not happen at exactly the same age for everyone, for example learning to walk.

3   Ask the children if anyone knows the word that describes the stage when boys and girls begin to change into men and women. Write the word 'puberty' so that the children actually see it in written form.

4   In groups, ask the children to think of any physical changes that happen to boys and girls during puberty.

5   Review the group work by asking the class to share what changes they have thought of and draw up two lists – one for boys and one for girls.

Girls	Boys
Sweat glands become more active	Sweat glands become more active
Breasts develop	Penis and testicles grow
Hips widen	Voice breaks
Body hair grows (pubic and underarm)	Body hair grows (pubic and underarm)
Growth spurt	Growth spurt
Menstruation (periods) starts	Wet dreams can occur

6   Emphasise that these changes occur at different ages for different people.

7   Invite the children to complete Activity Sheet 1 as a review of this activity and explain that they will continue to look at some of the changes that happen during puberty.

Resources
Photocopies of Activity Sheet 1

Extension activities
It is useful to have some information leaflets available for children to take home. You should be able to obtain these from your local Health Promotion Department or your school nurse may be able to help. Some manufacturers of sanitary wear provide leaflets free of charge.

The children can involve their families by asking them if they can remember any more details to fill in on the rungs of the ladder on Activity Sheet 1, for example how much they weighed, what time they were born and so on. It is important, however, to reassure the children that it does not matter if their families cannot remember details or do not have time to do this with them.

Climbing the ladder

Start at **The day I was born**, on the bottom rung of the ladder. Write in all the changes that have happened to you so far and the changes that will continue to happen until you reach **Grown up** at the top of the ladder.

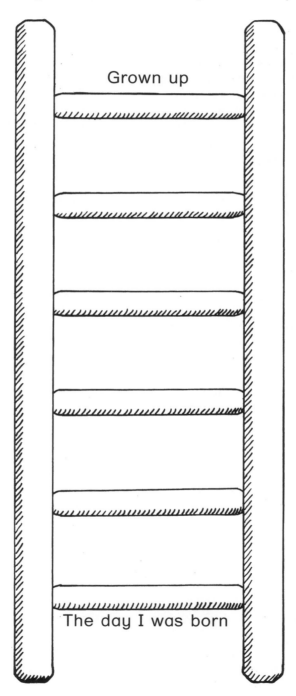

Grown up

The day I was born

The stage when a boy begins to change into a man and a girl begins to change into a woman is called **puberty**.

Blueprints PSHE and Citizenship Key Stage 2 © Judy Hunter and Sheila Phillips, Nelson Thornes Ltd, 2002

Growing and changing

2 Knowing the words

Aims
- To clarify the biological language for male and female sexual organs.
- To clarify the biological language for some aspects of sexual activity.

Teaching points
The language used by individual children and families will be wide and varied including some cultural words and words used as swear words. It is necessary to give children a common language and to make it clear that this is the language they will be encouraged and expected to use in school. Take care not to give the message that the words they may use at home are 'wrong', it is just that people make up different words to describe sexual organs and sexual activity, and that in school it is easier if everyone uses the same words so that we all know we are talking about the same thing. Review the ground rules before beginning this activity.

Instructions
1   Ask the children to work in small groups and to draw an outline of a person. (Alternatively, you can do this as a whole class or you can ask the children to draw round one person in each of their small groups and use that outline to write on.)

2   Ask the children to label as many parts of the body as they can think of (head, neck, arms, legs …).

3   Review the parts of the body with the class. If any have labelled sexual organs, acknowledge this. If not, discuss why they did not feel able to label these parts (embarrassment, because the gender of this person was not defined …).

4   Ask the children which external parts of the body are different for boys and girls and draw up two lists. Accept the language they give you and explain what words you are going to use. Write the words on the lists, making sure the children understand what parts of the body they refer to.

    Boys: penis, scrotum, testicles, foreskin
    Girls: breasts, vagina, clitoris, labia

5   Now ask the children what they think people might mean when they use the word 'sex'. Discuss how the word can be used to describe whether someone is male or female, the ways people show physical affection for each other and also to describe a man inserting his penis into a woman's vagina – this is called 'sexual intercourse' (write the words).

6   Explain that when two people are very attracted to each other they can have sexual feelings and when a man feels this, his penis becomes bigger and stiffer – this is called an 'erection' (write the word). When a woman has sexual feelings her vagina becomes moist and the penis can enter the vagina ('sexual intercourse'). Make it clear to the children that this is how a man and a woman produce a baby together.

7   Ask the children to work in groups to list ways people can show affection to each other without having sexual intercourse (kissing, holding hands, stroking each other, touching each other's sexual organs …).

8   Review the list and ask anyone if they have heard of the word 'masturbation' (write the word). Explain that when people go through puberty they begin to have sexual feelings and may begin to explore what their bodies feel like and what is happening to them by touching and stroking their sexual organs. Emphasise that this is perfectly normal and does not do any harm. It is done in private and is called masturbation. (If there are children present who think their religion says they should not masturbate, suggest they try to talk about it with their families or an older friend or with you privately.)

9   Invite the children to complete Activity Sheet 2 as a review of the lesson.

Resources
Photocopies of Activity Sheet 2

Extension activities
The school nurse may support you in delivering this aspect of PSHE. It may be easier to work with smaller groups rather than the whole class.

Name... Date ....

Knowing the words

Read the 10 statements or descriptions below. For each one, choose the correct word from the box which fits the description and write it in the space.

penis	vagina	testicles	scrotum	labia	clitoris
foreskin	masturbation		breasts	sexual intercourse	

1 The opening in a woman where the penis can be inserted. It goes from the uterus (or womb) to the outside.

....

2 The male sex organ, which becomes erect if a man is sexually excited.

....

3 The sac which holds the testicles outside the body.

....

4 The parts of the body which develop in females during puberty and contain milk glands.

....

5 Folds of skin outside the vagina.

....

6 The male sex organs which produce sperm and male sex hormones.

....

7 A sexual act between a man and a woman when the man's penis is inserted into the woman's vagina.

....

8 Thin skin that covers the end of the penis.

....

9 A female sex organ which produces feelings of excitement and pleasure.

....

10 Touching and stroking your own sexual organs for pleasure.

....

Growing and changing

3 Sperm meets egg

Aims

● To develop an understanding of the process of conception.
● To develop an understanding of how babies develop and are born.

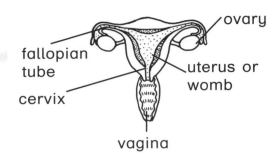

Teaching points

This activity follows on from 'Knowing the words' on page 4, once the children have been introduced to the words for the sexual organs and understand what is meant by sexual intercourse. The children may already have acquired some knowledge through science teaching, however it is important to start with what happens *before* conception, i.e. the penis goes into the vagina and sperm is released. Surprisingly, this is often overlooked and teaching begins with 'the sperm meets the egg'.

Instructions

1   Remind the children of the words used to describe the male and female sexual organs and the meaning of sexual intercourse (penis entering vagina).

2   Explain that they are now going to learn about the internal reproductive organs in males and females and how a baby begins and develops. Ask the children to look at Activity Sheet 3, which shows a woman's internal reproductive organs. Explain that a woman has two ovaries and, every 28 days or so, an egg is released from one of the ovaries and travels along the fallopian tube to the uterus (or womb). An egg can be fertilised, i.e. sperm joins with the egg, if a man and woman have sexual intercourse around the time when the egg is travelling along the fallopian tube. If the sperm and the egg join, the fertilised egg attaches itself to the lining of the womb and a baby begins to develop. If the sperm and egg do not join, i.e. if the egg is not fertilised, the egg is shed with the lining of the womb and that is what we call menstruation or having a period. Menstrual blood comes through the cervix (neck of the womb) and out through the vagina. Ask the children to label their diagram.

3   Use the second part of Activity Sheet 3 to help explain what a man's internal organs look like. Explain that when a man's penis becomes erect, if it is touched and stimulated, a man releases a small amount of fluid from the end of the penis, which is called semen. This contains sperm and if semen is released when the man's penis is inside a woman's vagina, the sperm can swim up the vagina and join with an egg in the fallopian tube. Sperm is stored inside the man's testicles. Ask the children to label their diagram.

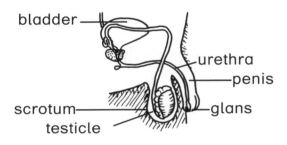

4   Remind the children that the word for the joining of sperm with an egg from which a baby grows is called 'conception'. It takes 40 weeks for a baby to grow before it is ready to be born. When a baby is born it comes out through the vagina, which stretches to make room for the baby to be born.

Resources

Photocopies of Activity Sheet 3

Extension activities

If a parent has recently had a baby perhaps she and/or her partner will talk to the class about what they had to do to look after the baby before it was born and how they care for the baby now. Alternatively, a local midwife or the school nurse could do this.

Sperm meets egg

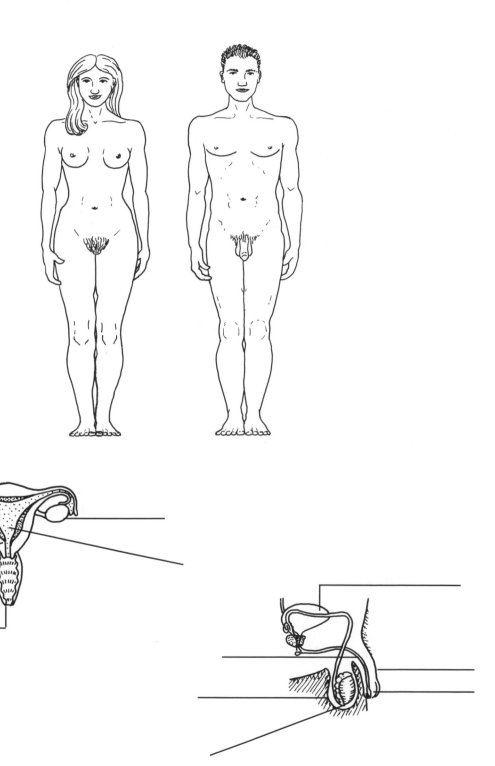

The word for the joining of sperm with an egg from which a baby grows is called **conception**.

Growing and changing

4 How is it for you?

Aims
- To understand some of the specific issues that arise in puberty for boys and girls.
- To dispel some of the myths about male and female sexuality.

Teaching points
You could offer a single-sex session each for the boys and girls if you think they would explore issues and questions in greater depth this way. It is important, however, that they also discuss the issues covered by this activity together so they can learn from each other. Try to keep your language as inclusive as possible, i.e. use the words 'relationship' and 'partner' rather than focusing on 'boyfriend/girlfriend'.

Instructions
1   Divide the class into small single-sex groups.

2   Ask the groups of boys to generate as many endings as they can think of for the statement 'As a boy I can …'

3   Ask the groups of girls to generate as many endings as they can think of for the statement 'As a girl I can …'

4   Review the above, managing the discussion to enable groups to put across their points of view and be heard fairly. Write up any key points that emerge.

5   Continue as above with all or as many of the following statements as you wish, giving just one statement at a time and reviewing the responses before moving on:

- 'As a boy I cannot …'
- 'As a girl I cannot …'

- 'If I was a boy I could …'
- 'If I was a girl I could …'
- 'Some of the things people say about boys are …'
- 'Some of the things people say about girls are …'
- 'When boys go through puberty they …'
- 'When girls go through puberty they …'

6   Discuss with the class which are the myths and which are the truths.

7   Invite the class to complete Activity Sheet 4, listing as many myths as they can think of for boys and girls in relation to puberty and in relation to being a boy/girl generally. At the end of the activity sheet, the children are asked to complete two statements and these can be shared with the class to generate further discussion or as a closing round (i.e. go round each member of the class inviting them to share their statement without comment from the rest of the class) – whichever is appropriate.

Resources
Photocopies of Activity Sheet 4

Extension activities
Explore the lifestyles of males and females in different countries and cultures, focusing on some of the rituals and ceremonies that take place around puberty.

Ask the girls to write 'A day in the life of …' (or 'A week in the life of…') imagining they are boys and the boys to do the same imagining they are girls. Discuss some of the assumptions and images that emerge from their writing and use them for further discussion with the class.

Name .... Date ....

How is it for you?

What are some of the things you have heard about being a girl or being a boy that you think are not true? Write them below.

Myths about being a boy

Myths about being a girl

....

....

....

....

....

....

....

....

Complete the following statements.

The best thing about being a boy is   The best thing about being a girl is

....

....

Blueprints PSHE and Citizenship Key Stage 2 © Judy Hunter and Sheila Phillips, Nelson Thornes Ltd, 2002

Growing and changing

5 Menstruation/having periods

Aims
- To develop an understanding of the process of menstruation and the menstrual cycle.
- To dispel some of the myths associated with menstruation.

Teaching points
Girls should be given the opportunity to discuss menstruation in more detail in a single-sex group. However, it is also important to ensure that boys understand the information contained within this activity. The school nurse may be able to offer a further session with the girls, allowing you time to work with the boys to answer questions about menstruation and go into more detail about wet dreams and masturbation, for example. There may be issues in relation to delivery of sex education by a female or a male teacher only – wherever possible it is helpful for the children to be able to seek further advice or clarification from both a male and female adult.

Instructions
1   Read Information Sheet 47 with the class, explaining in more detail anything the children do not understand.

2   Divide the class into small groups, and invite the children to complete the quiz on Activity Sheet 5.

3   Review answers, allowing plenty of time for discussion and further questions and providing additional information where appropriate.

Quiz answers:

1   *True*

2   *False* (The regularity of a girl's periods may vary considerably when she first starts menstruating.)

3   *True* (They vary considerably from woman to woman.)

4   *False*

5   *True* (A girl can continue with her usual lifestyle. Some girls do not feel like being very active during their period and others find that exercise can actually help to relieve any discomfort. A warm bath can also relieve discomfort and there is no reason not to bath.) N.B. Some religions may stipulate that a woman should not bath during her period.

6   *False* (Menstruating affects different women in different ways.)

7   *True* (Remember this is the 'average' and everyone is different.)

8   *True* (Varies from a very mild sort of ache to something more painful.)

9   *True* (Varies from woman to woman. If periods are very heavy it is best to ask the doctor for advice.)

10   *True*

Resources
Photocopies of Activity Sheet 5
Photocopies of Information Sheet 47

Extension activities
Some sanitary wear manufacturers will provide free samples for girls, many of which contain excellent information leaflets. Your local Health Promotion Department may also be able to provide leaflets or your school nurse may be able to help. Remember that boys need information to take away and read as well! If you prefer to use your own information sheets or leaflets, you could work with the school that your children feed into and ask some children to design and make a leaflet to meet the needs of younger children. (This would provide plenty of links with English, PSHE, ICT, Art and Design, with opportunities for some good transition work.)

Name.. Date ....

Menstruation/having periods

Tick one box for each statement.

		True	False	Don't know
1	Menstruation is a word used to describe when a girl has a period.	☐	☐	☐
2	Periods always come every 28 days.	☐	☐	☐
3	A period usually lasts between 3–7 days.	☐	☐	☐
4	Boys have periods as well as girls.	☐	☐	☐
5	It is fine for girls to have a bath, wash their hair and do exercise when they have a period.	☐	☐	☐
6	Girls/women are always moody or bad tempered when they have a period.	☐	☐	☐
7	The average age for a girl to start having periods is between the ages of 12 and 14.	☐	☐	☐
8	Most girls/women have a certain amount of discomfort before or during their periods.	☐	☐	☐
9	A girl loses about 2 tablespoons or half a small cupful of blood when she menstruates.	☐	☐	☐
10	Menstruation is a normal process, not an illness.	☐	☐	☐

Medicines and drugs

6 Medicines that help

Aims
- To develop an understanding that some people need to take medicines to help them combat illnesses.
- To develop an understanding of the different forms that medicines come in.
- To develop an understanding of the safe use of medicines.

Teaching points
This is an opportunity to help the children understand why some children may need to take medicines in school and to explore the safe storage and use of medicines in school.

Instructions
1   Ask the children if they have taken medicine when they have been ill.

   - Can they remember what they took the medicine for?
   - How did they know it was safe to take the medicine?

2   What forms does medicine come in? (tablets/pills, powder, syrup or mixture, spray, ointment, cream, lozenges, injections, drops) Write the answers on the board.

3   Discuss with the children how all these different forms of medicine can help to make us better when we are ill. Ask:

   - Can you remember a time when you have been ill and have felt better after taking medicine?

   - Why do some people need to take medicine all the time? (Some people have illnesses that cannot be cured permanently, for example asthma, diabetes, but their condition can be controlled with the use of medicine.)

4   Discuss in what ways we need to make sure that medicines are kept safe and taken safely. What can happen if they are not kept and taken safely?

   - Explain how medicines are kept safe in school and any rules surrounding the use of medicine.
   - Draw up a list of do's and don'ts on the board, inviting the children to share their ideas.

5   Invite the children to complete Activity Sheet 6 by drawing up their safety rules for the safe use of medicines.

Resources
Photocopies of Activity Sheet 6

Extension activities
Invite a pharmacist to talk to the class about his/her job and the safe use of medicines. It is helpful for the children to understand that pharmacists can give advice.

Link with citizenship: Discuss why people pay prescription charges and how this is part of our National Health Service. The children can be encouraged to think about all the services we receive and how they are paid for.

Medicines that help

Write below your list of safety rules for storing and taking medicines safely.

When you are writing them, think about how you would tell someone who knew nothing at all about storing and taking medicines safely, what the rules are. Make them as clear as possible. You could try showing them to another child in your class to see if he/she understands them clearly.

My rules for storing and taking medicines safely.

Blueprints PSHE and Citizenship Key Stage 2 © Judy Hunter and Sheila Phillips, Nelson Thornes Ltd, 2002

Medicines and drugs

7 Drugs that can harm

Aims

- To raise awareness that not all drugs can be taken safely.
- To convey the message that a drug is not always a medicine.
- To develop an understanding that alcohol and tobacco are drugs.

Teaching points

The issue that alcohol and tobacco are drugs needs to be explored sensitively so as not to frighten the children whose families drink alcohol or smoke. Consider the rules you have about smoking and drinking alcohol on school premises. Are you giving out consistent messages? (Are these being observed by the staff?)

Instructions

1   Ask the children whether they think there is a difference between medicines and drugs. What do people usually mean when they talk about drugs?

2   Remind them that medicines can be harmful if we do not take them safely. Explain that some people take drugs for other reasons than to help them to get better when they are ill and this can also be very harmful. Ask the children if they know of any reasons why people might take these drugs.

    Explain that these are known as 'recreational drugs' (write it on the board) and that they change the way people feel.

3   On the board write:

    A medicine is always a drug, but a drug is not always a medicine.

    - Draw up a list of any drugs like this that the children have heard of. (If they do not mention alcohol and tobacco, explain that these are also drugs and add them to the list.)

N.B. Don't worry if the children come up with words for drugs that you are unfamiliar with – the aim is to explore the safe use of drugs and you do not need detailed knowledge of drug information to put this point across.

- Ask the children how they might know that a medicine or drug is not safe to take. Write their ideas on the board.
- Ask the children why they think people take drugs when they can be harmful. If you prefer, divide the class into two groups and set up a debate, with one group putting forward a case for allowing people to take drugs and the other group putting forward a case for not allowing people to take drugs.

4   Invite the children to complete Activity Sheet 7 by filling in the blanks in the statement at the top of the page and then circling any of the drugs on the page that they think are **not** medicinal. Finally, ask the children to draw/write in any more drugs that they know, once again putting a circle around any that they think are not medicinal. (N.B. Heroin is usually seen as a drug that is misused, but it is also used medically to help people in pain. It should only ever be used when it is given by medical staff for the purpose of helping someone.)

5   Review Activity Sheet 7 with the class, encouraging them to share their ideas of other drugs they have thought of. Clarify which ones are **not** medicinal.

Resources

Photocopies of Activity Sheet 7

Extension activities

The police service may run a drugs education programme for schools in your area and may be able to offer some classroom sessions, particularly in relation to illegal drugs. This topic can be further supported by science teaching, for example the effects of drugs on your body.

Drugs that can harm

Fill in the blanks in the sentence below.

A medicine is always a d __ __ __ **, but a drug is not always
a m** __ __ __ __ __ __ __ .

Drugs are used in two different ways:

 They are used medically to cure illness, stop infection or ease pain.

 They are used as recreational drugs to change the way a person feels.

Look at the words and pictures below. Circle the drugs that you think are
used as 'recreational drugs'.

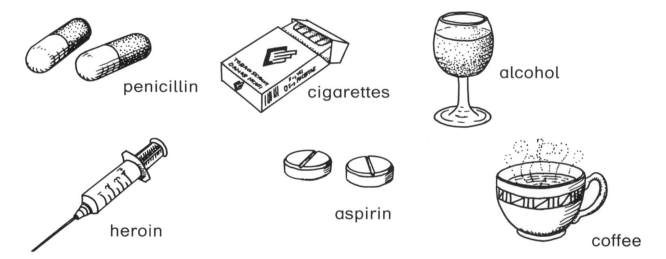

penicillin cigarettes alcohol

heroin aspirin coffee

Now draw and write in the name of any other drugs you can think of
below. Circle any that you think are used as recreational drugs.

Medicines and drugs

8 What should I do?

Aims
- To develop an understanding of the safe use of drugs.
- To encourage the children to consider the possible consequences of their actions for themselves.
- To enable the children to reflect on the responsibility they have for keeping themselves safe.

Teaching points
Children need to understand that as they grow older they have an increasing responsibility to keep themselves safe. This is part of growing up and becoming an adult. Any drug, even medicine, can be dangerous if misused.

Instructions
1   Invite the children to work in pairs or small groups to discuss each scenario on Activity Sheet 8 and decide what they should do in each case. Encourage them to consider the possible consequences of different courses of action and to decide what would be the safest thing to do.

2   Review Activity Sheet 8 with the class, agreeing on the most appropriate course of action for each scenario and discussing possible consequences of different options.

Resources
Photocopies of Activity Sheet 8

Extension activities
The children can demonstrate what they would do for each statement by role-playing their solutions.

Invite the children to compile a quiz based on the scenarios and the different solutions that are generated, for example 'Would you a) ... b) ... c) ...' . This could be used to raise awareness among parents of the topic you are covering and you could enlist their support in reinforcing messages.

If you are arranging a visit from a pharmacist, the children could complete the activity sheet before the visit as preparation for discussion topics.

What should I do?

Think carefully about the scenarios below. For each one, write what you think the safest course of action would be.

1 Someone says, 'I felt ill like that once and I took this medicine which really helped. Here, try this.'

....

....

2 You have a sore throat and a cough. Your older brother has some medicine left from when he had a sore throat recently and you think it might help you.

....

....

3 The doctor gives you some medicine and tells you to take it regularly every day until you have finished the bottle. After taking half of it, you feel better and don't know whether to keep on taking it.

....

....

4 Your doctor has prescribed some medicine that you have to take every morning and every night. One morning you forget to take it and wonder if you should just take twice as much that night to make up for it.

....

....

Blueprints PSHE and Citizenship Key Stage 2 © Judy Hunter and Sheila Phillips, Nelson Thornes Ltd, 2002

Medicines and drugs

9 Look, listen, think

Aims
- To enable the children to recognise stereotypical images in relation to drug misuse.
- To develop an understanding that some drugs are illegal and can be dangerous.
- To explore attitudes about illegal drugs and the people who may use or misuse them.

Teaching points
It is important to explore the images children may have of people who misuse drugs and enable them to realise that they may not be able to tell by looking at someone whether they misuse drugs or not. They therefore need to take responsibility for themselves and keep alert to possible dangers.

Instructions
1 Divide the class into small groups or pairs. Ask each group or pair to draw a picture of a person who uses drugs that he/she should not use (i.e. illegal drugs), and to write around the person any words they would use to describe something about his/her lifestyle, what he/she looks like, what job he/she might do, how old he/she is and so on.

2 Invite the groups to share their drawings and build up a common picture on the board of what this person or kind of person looks like. Explore with the children why they came up with their images, for example male/female, young/old, clean/dirty …

3 Now invite the class to draw a picture of someone who gives or sells illegal drugs to other people (a drug 'pusher') and to write words to describe this person.

4 Repeat Instruction 2 above.

5 Explain to the class that you are now going to give them a picture of a drug user and a drug pusher and you want them to compare them with the two drawings on the board. Distribute Activity Sheet 9.

6 Discuss the comparisons the children make, emphasising that a drug user or a drug pusher can look like anyone else. Discuss the meaning of the word 'stereotype' and how the media often portray people in stereotypical ways.

7 Now ask the children to think about how easy/difficult it would be to refuse to take something from someone who looked like a stereotypical drug pusher. How easy/difficult would it be to refuse to take something from someone who looked like their drawings? How easy/difficult would it be to refuse to take something from someone who they really trusted, for example their best friend?

8 Invite the children to complete the second part of Activity Sheet 9 by writing in why they think people take illegal drugs and why people give or sell other people illegal drugs.

9 Review Activity Sheet 9 with the class.

Resources
Photocopies of Activity Sheet 9

Extension activities
Link with citizenship: Explore the ways in which people might try to get money to buy illegal drugs and the possible consequences this has in relation to crime. Children could design some 'Look out' posters showing different images of illegal drug users/pushers to convey the message that it is important to share information with a responsible adult if they think someone may be using or selling drugs.

Look, listen, think

This is someone who uses illegal drugs.

This is someone who gives or sells people illegal drugs – a drug pusher.

likes watching sport

intelligent

pretty

has a good job

smart

has a wife and child

clean

drives a car

has a boyfriend

keeps fit

likes reading

lives with her mother and father

Write reasons why people might take illegal drugs.

....

....

Write reasons why people might give or sell other people drugs.

....

....

Medicines and drugs

10 Taking the risk

Aims
- To develop some understanding of the risks associated with taking illegal drugs, alcohol and tobacco.
- To understand that discarded syringes and needles can be dangerous.
- To explore attitudes to and beliefs about alcohol and tobacco use.

Teaching points
Make sure that the children understand what to do in school if they find discarded syringes, needles, solvents, alcohol, tobacco, illegal substances or medicines not stored safely. Check your school drug education policy and guidelines for dealing with drug-related issues. It is important not to ignore the fact that many children will see the attractions of using illegal drugs, drinking alcohol and smoking. Instead acknowledge these and help children to understand the balance against potentially very serious health and social issues.

Instructions
1   Explain to the children that although alcohol and tobacco are not illegal drugs they can still cause harm to our bodies and our health. Ask them if they have heard anything about the effects of smoking on people's health. (List these on the board.)

2   Now ask the children for anything they have heard about the effects of drinking alcohol on people's health. (List these on the board.)

3   Finally, ask them for anything they have heard about the effects of using illegal drugs on people's health. (List these on the board.)

4   Go on to ask them if there are any good things about drinking alcohol, smoking, using illegal drugs (for example people enjoy it, it helps people to relax, it is socially acceptable), and list these on the board.

5   Invite the children to complete Activity Sheet 10 by writing in the possible harmful effects on people's health and the positive aspects of smoking, drinking alcohol and taking illegal drugs.

6   Discuss with the class any other possible consequences, for example on the environment or on society. Invite the children to add these to the list on Activity Sheet 10.

7   Encourage the children to share their views about why people still smoke, drink alcohol and use illegal drugs despite all the risks attached to them.

8   Finally, ensure the children fully understand the school rules in relation to finding any substances in school or finding any equipment such as syringes or needles. Discuss what they should do, who they should tell, and who they could tell outside school if they found something potentially dangerous.

Resources
Photocopies of Activity Sheet 10

Extension activities
Link with citizenship: There are plenty of opportunities here to explore the cost to society of alcohol and tobacco use. Ask the children to come up with some ideas for what they feel would help to deter young people from starting to smoke and drink alcohol, and invite someone from your local health authority or local Health Promotion Department to listen to and discuss their ideas. If parents and visitors smoke around the boundaries of the school, for example when waiting to collect their children from school, the children could display some notices and devise an information campaign to encourage them to stop.

Name .... Date ....

Taking the risk

Write in below all the ways you can think of that smoking, drinking alcohol or using illegal drugs can harm your health.

....

....

....

....

....

Write in below everything you can think of that people might see as good things about smoking, drinking alcohol or using illegal drugs.

....

....

....

....

....

Apart from damaging people's health, how else can smoking, drinking alcohol or using illegal drugs be harmful? Write your ideas in the bubbles.

Blueprints PSHE and Citizenship Key Stage 2 © Judy Hunter and Sheila Phillips, Nelson Thornes Ltd, 2002

Keeping safer

11 Assessing the risk

Aims

- To develop the skill of assessing risks in different situations.
- To develop a sense of personal responsibility for keeping safe.

Teaching points

The skill of risk assessment can be applied to a range of health education and citizenship issues and is especially pertinent to the section 'Medicines and drugs' on pages 12–21. There are a range of organisations and initiatives that can support this aspect of your curriculum, for example local environmental health departments, the police service and the fire brigade. Many schools already run cycling safety programmes and road safety programmes. They will also focus on specific safety issues at appropriate times of the year, for example during the weeks leading up to Bonfire Night. If your school doesn't, you could explore what is available in other schools in your area.

Instructions

1   Draw a picture of a syringe on the board (or write the word 'syringe'). Ask the children when or how this object might be safe and when it might be dangerous. Discuss why in each case, emphasising that it is how the object is used or misused that makes it either safe or dangerous.

2   Write on the board the words 'crossing the road' and ask the children when this situation could be safe and when it could be dangerous. Discuss why in each case, emphasising that it is how someone responds to a particular situation that can make it safe or dangerous.

3   Invite the children (individually or in pairs) to complete Activity Sheet 11 by writing when an object or situation could be safe and when it could be risky or dangerous.

4   Review the activity by inviting the children to share their answers and discuss each object or situation in turn.

Resources

Photocopies of Activity Sheet 11

Extension activities

Working in small groups, the children can carry out a risk assessment exercise in different areas of the school. Ask them to identify potential risks (for example hanging cables, loose carpeting) and to report back on what they feel are the main risks, with suggestions on what could be done to rectify them. The children could write a report on their findings and recommendations to give to school governors.

Name.. Date ....

Assessing the risk

Look carefully at the objects below. Write what could make each one safe to use and what could make each one risky or dangerous to use.

	When this could be safe	When this could be dangerous
	....	....
	....	....
	....	....
	....	....

Think about the situations below. For each one write what could make it safe and what could make it dangerous.

Walking home from school

....

....

Playing on the beach

....

....

Walking near a railway

....

....

Blueprints PSHE and Citizenship Key Stage 2 © Judy Hunter and Sheila Phillips, Nelson Thornes Ltd, 2002

Keeping safer

12 What am I risking?

Aims
- To develop the skills of risk assessment and decision making.
- To develop an understanding of potential consequences to the decisions we make.
- To raise awareness of emotional and physical safety.
- To consider how their decisions can impact on other people.

Teaching points
The aim of safety education is to enable children to learn to take responsibility for keeping themselves as safe as possible, both now and in the future. To do this they need to learn the skills of risk assessment and decision making so that they can think for themselves and not just follow safety rules that are given to them.

Instructions
1   Ask the class to think of all the decisions they have made for themselves today or in the last week, for example what to wear, what television programme to watch, which way to walk to school, what to eat, who to talk to ...

2   Discuss how we all make decisions and that, as we grow older, we begin to make more and more decisions for ourselves. Some of these decisions will be easy to make and will involve very little risk. Other decisions will need to be considered carefully as there will be some risks attached to them.

3   Explain that you are going to consider some of the possible risks attached to 'smoking a first cigarette' (write this on the board). What could be a) the physical risks and b) the emotional risks to deciding to smoke a first cigarette? (The children may need some help in understanding that the decisions we make can affect the way we feel about ourselves.) List their ideas on the board.

N.B. If you feel this element of the activity is not appropriate to the age and maturity of the class, just focus on the physical risks.

4   Invite the children to share their ideas about how the decision whether or not to smoke a first cigarette can affect other people, and list these ideas on the board.

5   Invite the children to complete Activity Sheet 12 either individually or in small groups. If they work in groups encourage them to discuss each decision first before completing the activity sheet.

6   Discuss potential risks in the examples given on the sheet and help the children to consider how the decisions they make can also affect other people.

Resources
Photocopies of Activity Sheet 12

Extension activities
Link with citizenship: Expand this topic to enable the children to consider individual and collective decision-making processes. In what ways are collective decisions made? What decisions are made on our behalf by the government? How can we influence these decisions? Take one decision that is made on our behalf and map out in what ways that decision can affect other people.

What am I risking?

Consider each of the decisions below. For each decision, write what could be: a) the physical risks, b) the emotional risks and c) the possible effects on other people.

What shall I do?

What are the possible risks?

Decision about whether or not to play truant

a) ....

b) ....

c) ....

Decision about whether or not to try a substance given to you by your best friend

a) ....

b) ....

c) ....

Decision about whether or not to try a substance given to you by a stranger

a) ....

b) ....

c) ....

Decision about whether or not to lie to your parent/carer about where you are going

a) ....

b) ....

c) ....

Decision about whether or not to drink alcohol with your friends

a) ....

b) ....

c) ....

Blueprints PSHE and Citizenship Key Stage 2 © Judy Hunter and Sheila Phillips, Nelson Thornes Ltd, 2002

Keeping safer

13 Please don't tell

Aims

- To develop an understanding of the possible dangers of keeping inappropriate secrets.
- To explore the kinds of secret it may be important to share with others.
- To enable the children to appreciate that they have both rights and responsibilities in relation to their bodies and their emotions.

Teaching points

This is a sensitive issue, but an important one to raise. Make sure you are fully up-to-date with the school child protection procedures and be alert to any signs of concern the children may show and any disclosures they may make.

It is not sufficient for children to be aware of 'Stranger Danger' issues. Without causing alarm, they must also be made aware that it is not OK to keep a secret about close friends or even their own family if they themselves or another may be harmed.

Instructions

1   Invite the children to work in pairs to share with each other a secret wish or dream that they have.

2   Ask if anyone would like to share his/her secret wish/dream with the rest of the class.

3   Discuss with the class whether they would share any secret with the whole class. Why/why not? What secrets or kind of secrets would it feel OK to share?

4   Explain that sometimes it is really nice to share a secret with a friend, but that at other times it might not be safe to keep a secret. Ask the children what kinds of thing they think it might not be safe to keep secret, and write these on the board.

5   Discuss what the possible risks might be in keeping these things secret. Ask the following questions:

- Is it different when an adult asks you to keep a secret? Why/why not?
- Is it different when a close friend or a member of your family asks you to keep a secret? Why/why not?

6   Invite the children to complete Activity Sheet 13, either individually or in pairs.

7   Review the activity by inviting them to share their ideas. Emphasise the message that if someone touches them in a way that they do not like or hurts them, they should tell someone about it.

Resources

Photocopies of Activity Sheet 13

Extension activities

Link with citizenship: Who helps us? Draw up a chart of people within the community that the children could go to for help if they felt unsafe in any way. Display useful telephone numbers, such as Childline in the classroom.

Raising self-esteem – ask every child to say something positive about the person next to them, starting with the words 'I am going to tell you a secret ...' . Explore with the children how they can help each other to be positive about themselves.

13

Activity Sheet

Please don't tell

Here are some secrets you might be asked to keep. Which secrets do you think it would be OK to keep and which secrets do you think it would not be OK to keep? Write what you would do in each situation and why.

Please don't tell anyone that I failed the English test.

What would you do? ....

Why would you do it? ....

Please don't tell anyone I hit you.

What would you do? ....

Why would you do it? ....

Please don't tell anyone I have been using the Internet to talk in chat rooms.

What would you do? ....

Why would you do it? ....

Please don't tell anyone I have been touching you – they will not believe you anyway.

What would you do? ....

Why would you do it? ....

Please don't tell anyone I didn't understand the joke.

What would you do? ....

Why would you do it? ....

Please don't tell anyone I am taking alcohol to the party.

What would you do? ....

Why would you do it? ....

Blueprints PSHE and Citizenship Key Stage 2 © Judy Hunter and Sheila Phillips, Nelson Thornes Ltd, 2002

Keeping safer

14 Safety alert

Aims
- To enable the children to identify potential safety issues in the home and on the road.
- To develop an understanding of the ways in which the children can keep themselves safer at home and on the road.

Teaching points
There are some useful safety videos that can be used to generate discussion or to consolidate learning around this topic. Try contacting your local Health Promotion Department to see what is available.

Link with citizenship: This activity focuses on group work skills. The children will need to co-operate within and between groups to complete their task. It might be useful to first explore with the children how they intend to do this, so that everyone has a fair say and contributes equally.

Instructions
1   Divide the class into small groups and give each group a different topic to consider from the following list:

    - possible safety risks in the kitchen
    - possible safety risks in the bathroom
    - possible safety risks in other living areas of a house, including stairs
    - possible safety risks in the garden
    - possible safety risks as a pedestrian

    Ask each group to generate a list of all the risks they can think of for their allocated topic.

2   Review by asking each group to share its ideas and discuss what the biggest safety issues would be (you might want to limit this to 3–5 priority issues).

3   Now ask each group to discuss the biggest safety issues for their allocated topic and to agree ways in which they could be made safer, for example never leaving trailing cables in the kitchen, storing all garden tools securely.

4   Explain to the children that they are now going to prepare an information broadcast (TV or video) to raise people's awareness of possible safety risks in the home and on the road. Each group will have two minutes to inform people of the possible dangers and then to explain ways of reducing these risks.

    Develop this topic in as much detail as you feel appropriate. The children can be encouraged to present their information in different ways, for example by preparing accompanying visual material, pretending that one member of their group is a 'safety expert' and carrying out an interview with that person, by conveying information through an advert format or by composing a slogan or jingle.

5   Invite the groups to present their information broadcast. If equipment is available you may like to record the broadcast on video. Alternatively, you may like to invite some visitors to watch the broadcast and question the children about it.

6   Invite the children to complete Activity Sheet 14 to review the activity.

Resources
Photocopies of Activity Sheet 14

Extension activities
The children can prepare an information news-sheet for their parents on home and road safety issues, using the material they have prepared for their broadcast. This activity could also form the basis of a school assembly topic.

Safety alert

Now you have finished your TV or video broadcast on home and road safety, answer the following questions.

What did you enjoy most about this activity?

....

....

What did you not enjoy about this activity?

....

....

What safety message(s) do you remember?

....

....

....

What did you do to help prepare and present the broadcast?

....

....

....

How did your group work together? (Did members help each other and co-operate well? Were there any disagreements that the group had to sort out?)

....

....

....

Blueprints PSHE and Citizenship Key Stage 2 © Judy Hunter and Sheila Phillips, Nelson Thornes Ltd, 2002

15 Nice weather

Aims

- To develop an understanding of sun and water safety issues.
- To develop a sense of personal responsibility for keeping safe.
- To extend the children's range of emotional vocabulary.

Teaching points

It is important for children to see messages about sun safety put into practice in school, for example by encouraging them to wear protective clothing/sun cream in the sun and by witnessing adults in school doing the same. Children will learn far more by actually taking care of themselves than by being taught theoretically how to take care of themselves.

Instructions

1 Ask the children to imagine they are preparing for a trip to the beach or to an outdoor swimming pool on a hot sunny day. What would they be feeling?

   Gather words to describe these feelings on the board, encouraging the children to think of as many words as they can.

2 Now ask the children how they would prepare for the trip and what they would take with them. Write their ideas on the board.

3 Explain to the children that some of the things they would need to take are things that help them to keep safe. What would these things be? How would these things keep them safe?

4 Ask the children to imagine that they have arrived at the beach/swimming pool where they see two notices – one with instructions for keeping safe in the sun and one with instructions for keeping safe in or near water. Discuss what these instructions might be.

5 Invite the children to complete Activity Sheet 15, completing the two sets of instructions, one for sun safety and the other for water safety.

Resources

Photocopies of Activity Sheet 15

Extension activities

Extend this theme by asking children to plan a packed lunch for the day, containing a balanced meal and including some healthier options.

Link with science: Explore what skin is for.

Discuss why some people have different colour skin and what this means in terms of taking care of their skin in the sun.

(N.B. Be sure to convey the message that although people with very fair skin need to take extra care in the sun, people with darker skin and with black skin still need to protect themselves.)

Nice weather

Complete the notice. Write in your instructions for keeping safe in the sun.

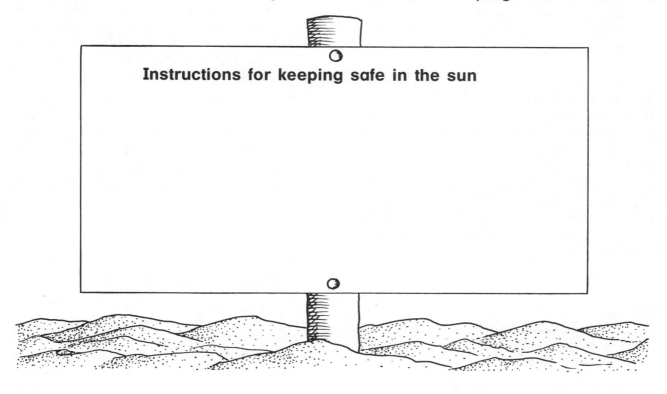

Instructions for keeping safe in the sun

Complete the notice. Write in your instructions for keeping safe in, or near, water.

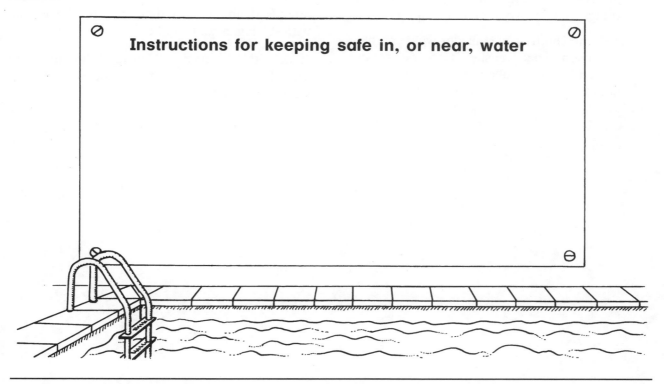

Instructions for keeping safe in, or near, water

Blueprints PSHE and Citizenship Key Stage 2 © Judy Hunter and Sheila Phillips, Nelson Thornes Ltd, 2002

Feelings and feeling good

16 Worry beads

Aims
- To explore some of the worries children may have.
- To enable the children to develop strategies for dealing with their worries.
- To encourage the children to express some of their worries.

Teaching points
Remember that what may seem a very small worry to us as adults, may be a huge concern to children. A child who is feeling overwhelmed by worries or difficult emotions will not be able to learn to the best of his/her ability. Therefore, it is important to deal openly with this topic and encourage children to share their worries and concerns in order to help them to realise their potential.

Instructions
1   Ask the class to consider the kind of things that people often worry about and write their ideas on the board.

2   Discuss whether some of these worries affect mainly people of a particular age group, for example children who are beginning to grow up. Are there some things we all worry about at some time?

3   Ask the children to consider what can help a person when he/she is worried about something and collect their ideas on the board.

4   Are there some worries that we can do something about and some worries that we cannot do anything about? Discuss with the children and explore what these might be.

5   Invite the children to complete Activity Sheet 16 by writing in any worries on the 'worry beads' that they or someone about the same age as them might have. For each worry, they can then write on a 'pearl of wisdom' what might help.

   N.B. Read through all the completed activity sheets carefully in case a child has any concerns that need to be dealt with. You may also want to offer the children the opportunity to talk through any of their worries with you individually. The school nurse may also offer some time.

Resources
Photocopies of Activity Sheet 16

Extension activities
Assemble a large set of 'worry beads' and 'pearls of wisdom' for display in the classroom, using the children's ideas.

Adapt this activity to 'angry beads' or 'sadness beads', i.e. 'things that I sometimes feel angry/sad about' and then 'pearls of wisdom' with strategies that can help.

Link with citizenship: Consider difficulties in school, in the community, in the country and strategies that could help.

Worry beads

Here is a set of worry beads. On each bead write a worry that you or someone about the same age as you might have.

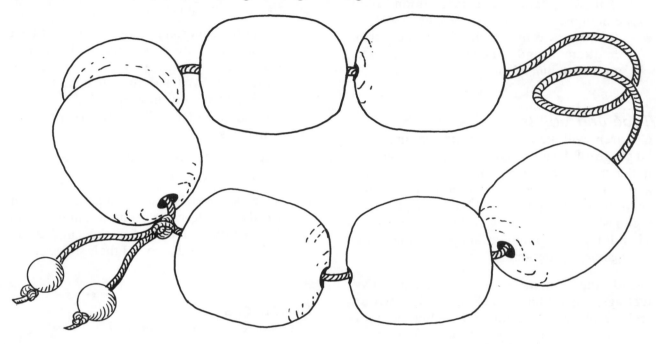

Here are some 'pearls of wisdom'. For each worry you have written on the worry beads above, try to think of some things that would help. Write your ideas inside the pearls of wisdom.

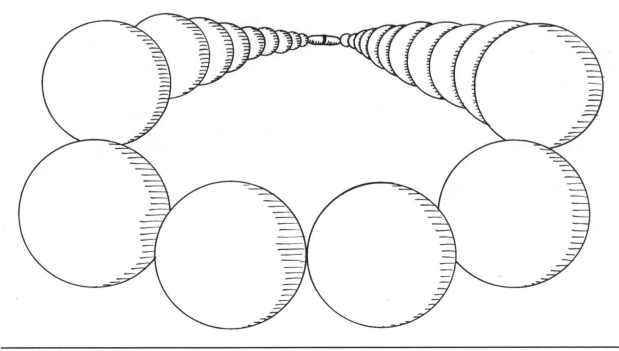

Feelings and feeling good

17 Shaping up

Aims

- To develop the children's vocabulary to include a language of emotions.
- To enable the children to have access to a wider range of emotional vocabulary when expressing and reflecting upon their emotions.
- To encourage the children to express their emotions and develop a greater understanding of them.

Teaching points

Children will benefit from developing their language of feelings and developing a greater understanding of them. Not being able to name and verbally express an emotion often leaves children with no alternative but to display their feelings through actions rather than words. Therefore, this is an important part of behaviour management programmes.

Avoid the language of 'positive/negative' feelings, 'good/bad' feelings, 'right/wrong' feelings. We all feel a range of feelings and it is unhelpful to class any of these feelings as negative or wrong. Clearly, however, we must help children to see that the actions they choose as a result of their feelings can be unacceptable or wrong, and we need to support them in finding more appropriate courses of action. This activity provides links with citizenship.

Instructions

1   Write the word 'angry' on the board. Ask the children to think of a time when they felt angry. Invite anyone who wants to share this with the class to do so.

2   If the word angry was a shape, can anyone think what kind of a shape it would be?

    (Children will have different ideas, but often it is a very jagged, sharp shape.) Draw their ideas for shapes on the board or invite individual children to do so.

3   Point out that there are other words we also use to describe being angry – some might mean 'just a little bit angry', others 'very angry'. Ask the children whether they can think of any of these words and write them on the board. (Add some of your own to extend the children's vocabulary, exploring the meaning of each one.)

4   Invite the children to look at Activity Sheet 17 on which the word 'angry' is given a shape and words related to anger are written around it. Ask them to complete the activity sheet by drawing suitable shapes around the other feeling words (happy, sad, worried, scared).

5   Ask the children what shapes they thought of for different words.

6   Take each word in turn and generate other words to describe that feeling as in Instruction 3 above. Ask the children to write these words around their shapes.

Resources

Photocopies of Activity Sheet 17

Extension activities

Display the shapes and extended vocabulary in the classroom as a reminder to the children.

Invite the children to write some sentences using some of the feeling words.

Encourage the children to share their emotions by asking them to finish some statements such as:

'A time when I was sad was ...'
'Something that makes me really happy is ...'
'I sometimes get worried when ...'
'When I was younger, I used to be scared of ...'

Shaping up

The word 'angry' has been written in a very sharp, jagged sort of shape. Read the words around the shape. They can also be used to describe feeling angry.

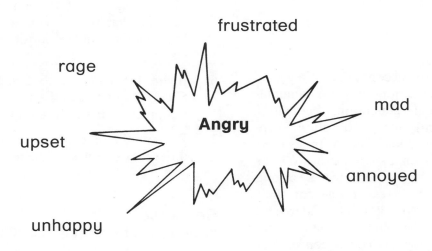

frustrated

rage

upset

Angry

mad

annoyed

unhappy

Think of a shape for each of the words below and draw it around the word.

Happy

Sad

Worried

Scared

Feelings and feeling good

18 Why did I do that?

Aims

- To raise awareness that how we treat people, and what we say to them, has an effect on how they feel.
- To consider the responsibility we all have to choose appropriate responses to our feelings.
- To reflect on the possible consequences of our actions.

Teaching points

Helping children to accept that they are responsible for their actions is a fundamental aspect of emotional education, behaviour management and citizenship education. Very often, children, young people and at times even adults, believe that if what someone has said or done causes them to experience a strong emotion, that person is responsible for their actions. We need to help children to understand that they have choices over their actions and that they are responsible for any consequences that may follow as a result of their actions.

Instructions

1. Ask the children how it feels when they are criticised and write these words on the board.

2. Discuss how they might respond to criticism and why. (Help them to see the link between their feelings and their actions, for example 'I feel angry when I am criticised so I shout.' 'I feel upset when I am criticised so I sulk.')

3. Now ask the children how it feels when they are praised and write these words on the board. Again, explore how they might respond to praise and why.

4. Discuss whether they think they have any control over their responses. Why/why not? Explain that different people might feel differently about being criticised, and might respond in a different way, but that how we respond is always our own choice.

5. Write an example on the board to discuss with the class, for example:

   Someone calls me a name.
   I might feel ...
   I can respond by ...

   (invite responses from the class)

   Explore the possible consequences as a result of the different responses, reinforcing the message that if someone responds in a way that has serious consequences, this is his/her choice and responsibility and no one else's.

6. Invite the children to complete Activity Sheet 18 which uses the same format as the example you have given on the board.

7. Review the children's responses to the different examples on the activity sheet.

Resources

Photocopies of Activity Sheet 18

Extension activities

Use the same format as in Instruction 5 above to help the children to reflect on difficult situations that they have experienced in school (without mentioning names). Write what happened, how individuals felt, what choices they had about how to respond, how they decided to act and what were the consequences of their choices.

As you gather words to describe feelings (as in Instructions 1 and 3 above), display them around the classroom to reinforce vocabulary so the children have more words to choose from when expressing their feelings. You can display them in the form of leaves on a plant, petals on a flower, bricks in a house and so on.

Why did I do that?

For each of the following situations, write in how you might feel and how you could choose to respond. Give as many different feelings and responses as you can.

Now write which response might have the worst consequences and which response might have the best consequences.

● Someone pushes me over. I might feel ....
   I can respond by ....
   The response which I think might have the worst consequences is
   ....
   The response which I think might have the best consequences is
   ....

● Someone wants me to steal something. I might feel ....
   I can respond by ....
   The response which I think might have the worst consequences is
   ....
   The response which I think might have the best consequences is
   ....

● I get punished for something I did not do. I might feel ....
   I can respond by ....
   The response which I think might have the worst consequences is
   ....
   The response which I think might have the best consequences is
   ....

● I get told off for not doing my homework. I might feel ....
   I can respond by ....
   The response which I think might have the worst consequences is
   ....
   The response which I think might have the best consequences is
   ....

Feelings and feeling good

19 Up, up and away

Aims
- To raise individual and class self-esteem.
- To enable the children to reflect on what helps them and other people to feel good.
- To focus on the positive attributes of individuals.

Teaching points
Raising self-esteem raises motivation and achievement and is therefore an essential part of school life. Whilst this activity provides one means of focusing specifically on the issue, the greatest and most lasting impact will derive from the school ethos and consistency of values displayed by the school community. This activity is suitable for circle time.

Instructions
1   Ask the children what helps them to feel good about themselves. Write their ideas on the board.

2   Invite each child to say one thing that he/she is confident about doing really well. (If the children are comfortable with each other, ask them to give a round of applause after each one.)

3   Now invite every child to say one positive thing about the child next to him/her, for example something he/she likes about that child, something that child can do well, something positive that child contributes to the class.

4   Discuss with the children what it feels like saying something positive about themselves, and what it feels like hearing someone else say something positive about them.

5   Invite the children to complete Activity Sheet 19 by writing their positive qualities and skills inside the kites. (Some children may need extra encouragement and support.)

6   Ask the children what is good about their class as a whole, for example helping each other, taking turns, including everyone, being punctual, being polite. Write these ideas on the board.

7   End by asking everyone to finish the statement 'The best thing about being in this class is ...'.

Resources
Photocopies of Activity Sheet 19

Extension activities
Write the children's ideas on what is good about their class on a large kite shape for display purposes. Each child's name can be written on a piece of card and attached to the tail of the kite.

Encourage the children to consider what they could do even better as a class and to set targets to achieve this over the next few weeks. (Don't forget to review progress.)

Using the same format, encourage the children to reflect on what is good about being in their school. You could use this material as the basis for a school assembly.

Up, up and away

Think carefully about all the things that are good about you – perhaps you help other people, you have a nice smile, you are a good friend.

Now think about all the things you do well.

Write what is good about you and what you do well on the kites below. You can write more than one thing on each kite.

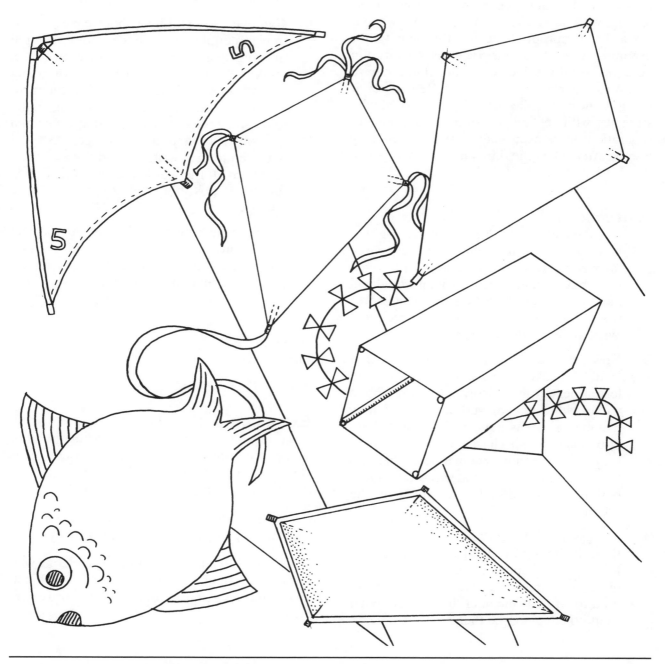

Feelings and feeling good

20 Sad is a feeling

Aims
- To explore the feelings associated with grief, loss and change.
- To enable the children to understand that everyone will experience such feelings at some point in their lives.
- To develop the skill of empathy.

Teaching points
This is a sensitive topic which needs to be discussed with the children. Usually children are far less reticent than adults in talking about such issues and do want to explore and share their feelings with others. There may be times when it would be inappropriate to use this activity, for example if a child has recently suffered a bereavement. In such cases ensure children have access to other means of support. Remember, it will not always just be the child concerned who struggles with feelings following bereavement, separation or change; other class members may also be affected by the difficulties of their peers.

Instructions
1   Ask the children to think of something that is very special to them (for example a favourite toy, a gift, something they saved up to buy) and to imagine what it would feel like to lose their special object. What words would they use to describe those feelings? Write their words on the board.

2   Now ask the children to imagine what it would feel like, or perhaps has felt like, to lose a person in their lives (for example a friend who has moved away, a family member who has gone to live somewhere else, someone special who has gone away for just a short time or someone special who has died). Invite the children to talk about how this feels and add any words on the board.

3   Discuss with the children how sometimes these feelings may change or be different, for example if someone has to go away for just a short time but will return, or if you get used to a family member living away. What would the feelings be then?

4   Discuss with the children how sometimes the feelings don't change so much, for example if someone dies we know we won't be able to see them again. Ask the children how they would help someone in such a situation and who they could talk to.

5   Explain to the children that there is also another kind of difficult feeling which we sometimes feel when things change in our lives and that this can feel a bit like losing something or someone. Ask them to think about when they first started school. This was a change in their lives. What were some of the feelings they felt then and what memories do they have of that time?

6   Talk with the children about changes that most people experience, for example moving house, changing school, growing up, making new friendships, breaking friendships and so on. Invite them to complete Activity Sheet 20 by writing on the path some possible changes that occur in a person's life and at what age. Ask the children to then write around the events on the path all the words they can think of to describe possible feelings about these changes.

7   Review the activity and highlight the fact that some of the changes, and feelings about them, that people experience in their lives are common to everyone.

Resources
Photocopies of Activity Sheet 20

Extension activities
Children's literature is an ideal starting point or a way of consolidating this topic as it can allow children to talk through characters in a story and distance themselves from their feelings.

Create or extend classroom displays with the vocabulary generated through this activity.

Ask the children to write a story of someone who lost and then found a special object, incorporating some of the 'feeling words' you have discussed.

Sad is a feeling

Write on the path all the changes you can think of that a person might experience during his/her life. For each change, write in the approximate age that you think the person might be.

Now use a different colour to write in all the different feelings you think he/she might feel each time.

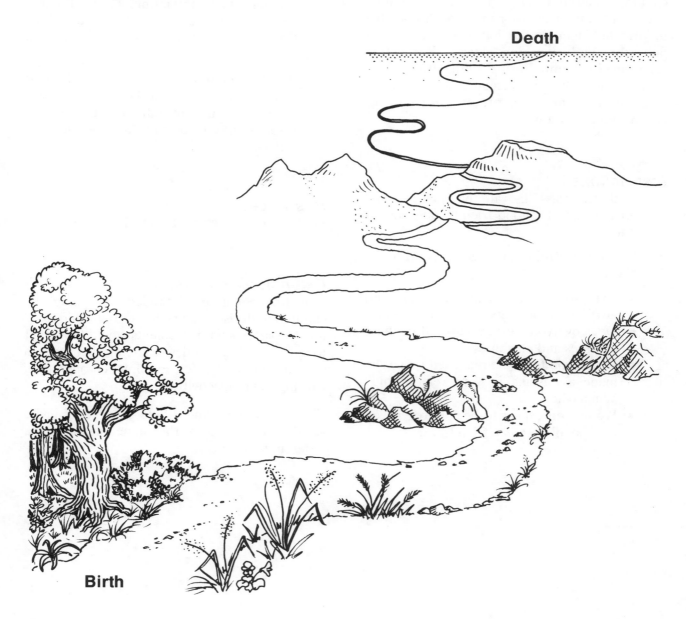

Death

Birth

Now you have finished writing in the changes and feelings, add some pictures around the path that help to describe the changes.

Blueprints PSHE and Citizenship Key Stage 2 © Judy Hunter and Sheila Phillips, Nelson Thornes Ltd, 2002

Friendships, families and being me

21 Come to the party

Aims

- To develop an understanding of the importance of friendships.
- To enable the children to reflect on the components of good and trusting friendships.
- To raise awareness of the responsibilities each of us has in our friendships.

Teaching points

Children need to develop the skills of initiating and maintaining friendships in order to be able to form and maintain relationships in their adult personal and working lives. Respecting relationships, empathising with others and having the skills to overcome difficulties in relationships are important aspects of citizenship education.

Instructions

1 With the class, list all the qualities and attributes that a good friend would ideally have.

2 Discuss the following questions with the class:

- Are some of these qualities and attributes more important than others?
- Does everyone always have all of these qualities and attributes?
- Would you forgive a real friend if he/she made a mistake in your relationship? When/when not?
- Would you expect to be forgiven if you made a mistake in a friendship?

3 Ask the class to work in pairs or small groups and to list 8 things that would be missing in their lives if they did not have friends, for example someone to talk and share things with, someone to walk to school with, someone to play sport with...

4 Review the above by asking the groups to share some of their ideas, emphasising that, because friendships add so much to life, it is important to value and care for them.

5 Invite the children to complete Activity Sheet 21 by imagining they are inviting someone to a 'Friendship Party'. Remind them to state clearly why they are inviting them, i.e. what they would contribute as a friend.

6 Ask the children to share their invitations with the class. Remind them that if this is what they value in a friend, they have a responsibility to be that kind of friend to others.

Resources

Photocopies of Activity Sheet 21

Extension activities

This theme can be extended by asking the children to devise a recipe for a 'friendship cake' for the party. What ingredients would they want to include? They can devise friendship games to play at the party, for example co-operation, trusting, sharing activities.

They could plan the whole party and invite another class (from the same school or a different school).

Come to the party

Imagine the kind of person you would like to invite to a 'Friendship Party'.
What would your friend be like? What qualities would make him/her a
special friend? Write the invitation below, explaining why you want him/her
to come to your party.

Please Come To My Friendship Party

You are invited to my friendship party

because you ....
....

The good thing about being friends with you is that

....
....

As a friend to you I will try to

....
....

From ....

Friendships, families and being me

22 In tandem

Aims
- To develop an understanding of both the contribution and responsibility we have within our family lives.
- To acknowledge the different structures of families and family groups that people live within.

Teaching points
Be sensitive to the many different kinds of families that children will be part of and encourage them to be similarly sensitive and empathetic. Try to make your language as inclusive as possible. If you have a multi-cultural mix of children, explore the different traditions and ways of life within the different cultures and family groups.

Instructions
1   Discuss with the children what 'family' means to different people. To some it might mean the people they live with, to others it might mean a wider group of people to whom they are related and to others still it might mean the people in their lives with whom they have a close relationship. Emphasise that some people live with a mother and father, some with neither; some have brothers/sisters, grandparents, some do not, etc.

2   Ask the children to imagine a typical day (for example a school day), from the time they wake up in the morning until they go to bed at night, and to write down all the things that their family members do for them. (Remember this may be different members in different families.)

3   Review by inviting the children to share some of the things their families do for them (without asking any individual child specifically).

4   Now ask the children to go back over the same day in their minds and, this time, to write down all the things they do for their families.

5   Review this by inviting the children to share some of the things they do for their families.

- Why is it important for family members to do things for each other?
- What would happen in a family if no one did anything for each other?
- Does anyone think they could do more to help their families? How?

6   Invite the children to complete Activity Sheet 22 by writing in all the things that their families do for them and all the things they do for their families.

Resources
Photocopies of Activity Sheet 22

Extension activities
Ask the children to imagine swapping roles for the day with a member of their family and to write 'A day in the life of' that person, describing what they think it would be like to be them.

Explore the role of the different genders in families in different cultures.

Discuss with the children why some people may choose to marry and some may not.

In tandem

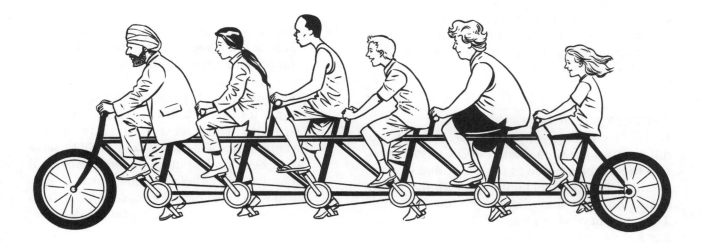

My family does these things for me

Think of all the things your family/family group does for you. Write these between the spokes of the wheel on the left.

Think of all the things you do for your family/family group and write these between the spokes of the wheel on the right.

I do these things for my family

Friendships, families and being me

23 Follow the leader?

Aims
- To explore when it may/may not be appropriate to stay loyal to a friend.
- To consider situations and decisions in life when it may be important to take responsibility for their own actions and choices.

Teaching points
It is often very difficult for children to differentiate between when it is OK to stay loyal to a friend and be 'one of the gang', and when it would be better (safer) not to go with the crowd but to do what they themselves think is right. They may have very mixed feelings; on the one hand they want to 'fit in' and be accepted by their peers, on the other their instincts are telling them that something is wrong. This activity provides links with citizenship.

Instructions
1. Start off with a game of 'Simon says ...' or 'Follow the leader ...'. This is where one person (the leader) starts an action, such as clapping hands, and everyone in the class must follow and do the same action. When the leader changes the action, for example stops clapping and starts waving with his/her right hand, everyone else follows. Different children can take turns at being the leader, or the teacher can lead.

2. Discuss with the children what kind of things they might find difficult to refuse to do when they are asked by a friend or leader of a gang, even though they know it might not be a good or safe thing to do. Ask the following questions:
   - What makes it difficult to say no?
   - What different feelings might you have?
   - What is the difference between being a loyal and good friend and being someone who just goes along with whatever their friend wants?

3. Divide the class into pairs or small groups and invite them to generate a list of things that a friend might ask them to do. At this stage, tell the children not to worry about whether or not it is OK to do these things.

4. Play another game of 'Simon says ...' or 'Follow the leader ...', this time asking one child from each group/pair to be the leader and to call out 3 things that a friend might ask them to do, for example 'A friend says ... come for tea'; 'A friend says ... try this cigarette'. Instruct the class to decide whether they will follow or not and to show their decision by putting their thumbs up if they will and their thumbs down if they won't. (Keep going for as long as it feels appropriate, giving each group/pair equal turns.)

5. Review by discussing with the class which suggestions they decided to follow and which they decided not to follow, and why. Why do people not always make the same decision? What could be some of the possible consequences of following the leader in some of the situations?

6. Invite the children to complete Activity Sheet 23 as a summary of the lesson, using examples of when they would/would not follow the leader.

Resources
Photocopies of Activity Sheet 23

Extension activities
Discuss with the class when 'following the leader' might/might not mean being bullied into doing something.

With the class, design a badge or certificate for 'Friend of the week'. Each week ask the class to suggest which class member should receive the award for that week and why. Present the award to that class member. (You may want to widen this to 'Citizen of the week'.)

23

Activity Sheet

Follow the leader?

'Simon says ...'   'Simon says ...'   'Simon says ...'

Write 6 things that a friend might ask you to do.

If you would **not** agree to do what your friend asked put a cross (✖) in the box. If you **would** agree to do what your friend asked put a tick (✔) in the box.

'A friend says ...'

☆1☆ .... ☐

☆2☆ .... ☐

☆3☆ .... ☐

☆4☆ .... ☐

☆5☆ .... ☐

☆6☆ .... ☐

Blueprints PSHE and Citizenship Key Stage 2 © Judy Hunter and Sheila Phillips, Nelson Thornes Ltd, 2002

Friendships, families and being me

24 It's good to be me

Aims
- To explore how every individual is unique and special.
- To enable the children to focus on the positive aspects of themselves.
- To develop a sense of self-worth and self-esteem.

Teaching points
It can be surprising how many negative images children of even a very young age can have about themselves. In endeavouring to help children to develop a sense of responsibility, maturity in their attitudes and an appropriate set of behaviours, we need to constantly and consistently work to develop within them a sense of self-esteem and self-belief.

Instructions
1   Invite the children to work in pairs to make a list of 5 things they have in common with each other. (This can be physical, for example both have black hair; it can be something they like, for example both like pizza; or it can be something about their lives, for example both live in a flat.)

2   Review by asking each pair to share one thing they found they had in common. Discuss whether these were always exactly the same, for example was it the same kind of pizza or exactly the same length/colour of hair?

3   Now invite the pairs to make a list together of 5 things they do not have in common with each other.

4   Review by asking each pair to say one thing they did not have in common.

5   Discuss with the class how, despite having some things in common with other people, everyone is unique and special in some way. People have different talents, skills and qualities. There is not a 'right' way to look or to be. Ask the class if anyone can think of something that is special about himself/herself. Ask the class if anyone can think of something that is special about someone else in the class. (Set some ground rules to ensure this is done in a supportive way.) Try to ensure that everyone either receives a positive comment or is able to say something positive about himself/herself.

6   Invite the children to complete Activity Sheet 24 by making up their special bottles of sauces by listing the 'ingredients' that make them special. These can be displayed on the classroom wall or the children can copy their ideas on larger pieces of paper for display.

Resources
Photocopies of Activity Sheet 24

Extension activities
Ask the class to move around the room, shaking hands with each person in turn, introducing themselves and saying one thing that they are really good at, for example 'Hello, my name is Alex and I am really good at playing computer games.'

Make a larger version of the activity sheet and compile a 'class bottle of sauce', listing something special about everyone in the class.

It's good to be me

Write your name in the space below.

Under the word 'Ingredients', write in the things that make you special and all the things that you do well and are proud of.

EXTRA SPECIAL SAUCE

_____

INGREDIENTS

This is a really special bottle of sauce because

....

....

....

Blueprints PSHE and Citizenship Key Stage 2 © Judy Hunter and Sheila Phillips, Nelson Thornes Ltd, 2002

Friendships, families and being me

25 It can be a bumpy ride

Aims
- To understand some of the difficulties that can arise in friendships and family relationships.
- To understand that everyone has responsibilities within their relationships.
- To consider ways of maintaining relationships and dealing with conflict situations.

Teaching points
It can be difficult for children to understand that they have a shared responsibility within their relationships, i.e. that good relationships are about give and take. They need to be supported in reaching this understanding and encouraged to widen their friendship circles to include members of the school community. Remember that some children come from very small family and friendship groups, whilst others are used to socialising in much larger family and friendship circles. Cultural experiences and expectations will also play a role, for example some children may be encouraged to keep their feelings private, others may be encouraged to share and express feelings readily. Gently encourage children to share their differences, respect differences and learn from those differences.

Instructions
1   Ask each child to draw a circle in the middle of a piece of blank paper and to write his/her name inside the circle.

2   Now invite the children to think about the people they are close to in their lives and to write the names of those people in circles around the circles that contain their own names. They can write them very close to their own names or further away, depending on how close a relationship it is.

3   Explore and discuss with the class the different kinds of relationships we have with people, for example family relationships (which may be close or very distant), friends, 'best' friends, relationships we may have through our religion, classmates, teachers, people we meet in social groups and so on. Ask:

- How are some relationships different to others?
- What can make some relationships more important to us than others?

4   Invite the children to think of ways in which relationships can sometimes become difficult and write their ideas on the board. Use some of the ideas, or some of the examples below, to explore with the class what can cause difficulties within a relationship and how those difficulties might be overcome:

- Relationship with a 'best' friend (possible difficulties: best friend forms a close relationship with someone else, arguments start because friends develop different social interests, and so on.
- Relationship with a mother/father/carer
- Relationship with a classmate
- Relationship with a fellow member of a club/society/team
- Relationship with a brother/sister/cousin.

5   Ask the children to complete Activity Sheet 25, based on a relationship in their lives. Ask them to think about possible difficulties that could arise in that relationship and then what they could do to try to overcome those difficulties.

Resources
Photocopies of Activity Sheet 25

Extension activities
Develop some of the ideas generated by the children in Instruction 5 above by asking the children to role-play some of the situations and the ideas for overcoming difficulties.

Make a collage/display of different types of relationships. Firstly, draw up a general list together of people that the children come into contact with (for example peers, family, friends, teachers, shopkeepers). Allocate a different person to each child. Ask each child to draw or make as detailed a picture as possible of that person. Use these to form a class display.

It can be a bumpy ride

This is ....

This is me

 1   Imagine you are the driver of the car. Choose a person you have a relationship with to be your passenger. Write in his/her name.

 2   Think of a difficulty that you might face in this relationship. Write what it is on the first part of the road that is uphill and bumpy.

- What could you do to try to resolve the difficulty? Write your ideas on the next part of the road, which is smooth and straight.

- Think of 2 more difficulties that might arise in the relationship. Write those difficulties on the other 2 parts of the road that are uphill and bumpy.

- What could you do to try to resolve the difficulties? Write your ideas on the other 2 parts of the road that are smooth and straight.

Blueprints PSHE and Citizenship Key Stage 2 © Judy Hunter and Sheila Phillips, Nelson Thornes Ltd, 2002

Looking good and keeping well

26 Round the clock

Aims
- To raise awareness that people have choices about developing healthy lifestyles.
- To encourage the children to take responsibility for making healthy choices.
- To develop an understanding of the benefits of exercise, hygiene and healthy eating.

Teaching points
Be careful not to be critical of children's lifestyles, for example their eating choices and levels of hygiene – children come from different backgrounds and will not all have the same level of access to healthy options. Focus particularly on what children can do during the school day to maintain a healthy lifestyle, for example choosing healthier lunch options, washing their hands, drinking plenty of water, exercising. This is an opportunity to also discuss different cultural practices in health and hygiene.

N.B. Adults and children need to drink plenty of water each day. Some studies report that children who are actively encouraged to drink water throughout the day show a rise in their learning retention rates. Try to provide water in the classroom.

Instructions
1   Either individually or in small groups, ask the children to draw a 'not so healthy person' and to write/draw around that person all the things that contribute to making that person not as healthy as he/she might otherwise be.

2   Review with the class by compiling the pictures and words describing a 'not so healthy person' on the board.

3   Now ask the children to draw a 'healthy person' and to write/draw around that person all the things that can help to make and keep that person healthy.

4   Review with the class by compiling the pictures and words describing a 'healthy person' on the board.

5   Discuss the 2 images with the children, if necessary helping them to broaden their concept of health to include resting, playing and taking care of their mental health, spiritual health, etc. Why do people sometimes make choices that are not so healthy? When is this OK/not OK? (For example, it is OK to eat sweets sometimes.)

6   In groups, ask the children to make a list of all the healthy choices they could make during a school day from the moment they get up in the morning till they go to bed at night.

7   Review and discuss the lists made by the groups. Encourage the children to include the occasional treat (watching television, a bar of chocolate and so forth) to emphasise that having a healthy lifestyle does not mean never having some of the treats that might not be good for us if we had too much of them.

8   Invite the children to complete Activity Sheet 26 by writing in around the clock the choices they could make during a typical school day to help them to stay as healthy as possible, for example 7:30 a.m. eating ... for breakfast. 8:00 a.m. brushing teeth, etc.

Resources
Photocopies of Activity Sheet 26

Extension activities
Explore the daily routines of people from different countries and cultures. What foods do they eat? What sports do people in different countries like to play? What are their religious beliefs? Go 'around the clock' writing in different daily routines for different people. Extend this to some daily/weekly diary entries. Explore the possibility of the children communicating with the children in a different country by email so they can compare lifestyles.

Round the clock

Think about a normal school day. What things do you do that help to make and keep you healthy?

Now think about what you **could** do during a normal school day that would help to keep you as healthy as possible. Think about the whole day from the moment you get out of bed to the time you go to bed again.

Write your ideas around the clock. For example, if you eat breakfast at 7:30 a.m. write in 'eat breakfast' and also say what you would choose for breakfast.

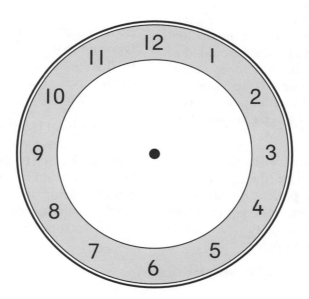

What would be the biggest treat you would give yourself during the day?

....

Looking good and keeping well

27 Doctor, Doctor

Aims

- To raise awareness that people have choices about developing healthy lifestyles.
- To develop an understanding of the benefits of exercise, hygiene and healthy eating choices.
- To consider the value of keeping healthy and ways to achieve this.

Teaching points

If you prefer, you can deliver this activity through role-play. The children can play the part of the doctor/patients. The scenarios could include family members talking about their concerns for the patients and what they feel could help them in the situation given. Be sure to emphasise that to a large extent people make their own decisions about health choices.

Instructions

1 Explain Activity Sheet 27 to the class. It has four different patients, each one describing a different problem to the doctor. Ask the children to imagine that they are the doctor and decide what each patient should do. They should write the solution down on the prescription pad for one of the patients. They should then write solutions for the other three patients on a separate sheet of paper.

2 Review each problem with the class, inviting children to share their ideas for what would help each patient. (You could draw up a list of all the options given for each of the four problems on the board and see which are the most popular.)

3 Depending on the depth of the discussion already generated, you could go on to explore the following:

- Could people do more to take care of their own health rather than going to the doctor for medicines? What kind of things would help?
- Why is hygiene so important? What should we do to keep ourselves clean?
- Why is it important to eat a balanced diet? What do you think would be a daily balanced diet?
- What happens to our bodies when we exercise? (Stress the importance of keeping the heart strong.)
- Why do you think people smoke even though it is bad for their health?
- Why do people drink too much even though it is bad for their health?

4 Ask the children to think of a 'prescription' for themselves – something that could help to keep them healthy – and invite them to say what this would be.

Resources

Photocopies of Activity Sheet 27

Extension activities

Draw up more patient problems for the children to discuss or ask the children to write some themselves. These can then be distributed around the class.

Ask your local Health Promotion Department or Health Centre for some leaflets on health issues that the children could use to help them with this task. This could be an opportunity to invite the school doctor to visit the class so that the children can ask questions about the role of a school doctor or a General Practitioner.

Doctor, doctor

Imagine that you are the doctor listening to these four patients. Choose one patient, 'prescribe a solution' to the problem by writing what you think he/she should do on the prescription pad. Write solutions for the other three patients on a separate sheet of paper.

First patient

Doctor, recently I have been growing very quickly. My mother says I am going through puberty. The problem is everyone at school says I really smell.

Second patient

Doctor, I always feel tired. My hair and skin look bad and my family tell me that I always look pale.

What do you eat and drink usually in a day?

I don't eat anything for breakfast, but I do have a can of pop and crisps on the way to school. For lunch I usually have chips and a bar of chocolate. On the way home from school I have some more pop and either a packet of crisps or chocolate. For tea, I usually have chips with fish fingers or pizza and biscuits and pop before bed.

Third patient

Doctor, can you please give me a letter to say I don't have to do PE at school? The teacher says I need to get fit because I get out of breath

really easily and I can't run. I don't do exercise or sport outside school because I don't like it, so why should I do any in school? I just want to watch TV and play on the computer.

Fourth patient

Doctor, can you please give me some tablets, I have a bit of a toothache and my teeth are going really brown. I have smelly breath as well. I don't want to go to the dentist. I've only been once and I didn't like it.

PRESCRIPTION
....
....
....
....
....
....
....
DR KNOWSBEST

Blueprints PSHE and Citizenship Key Stage 2 © Judy Hunter and Sheila Phillips, Nelson Thornes Ltd, 2002

Looking good and keeping well

28 Charged up

Aims

- To understand the importance of taking care of our mental and emotional health.
- To understand how taking care of our physical health can impact on our mental and emotional health.
- To appreciate different things can make different people feel well and happy.

Teaching points

This activity can be carried out at any time during Key Stage 2, but you may find it particularly useful as a preliminary activity to exploring the emotions and issues of transition from primary school. Appreciating that emotions change and that sometimes we feel fed up is also linked to puberty education.

Instructions

1   Ask the children to think of a time when they have felt very tired and unwell.

- What do you remember feeling?
- What did you feel like when you felt better?
- What happens to you? What do you do when you feel fed up?

2   Invite the children to complete Part A of Activity Sheet 28 by writing in words along the rays of the sun to describe things that make them happy.

3   Invite the class to share some of the things that make them happy and write these on the board. Emphasise that perhaps we won't feel really happy all of the time, but that it is nice to do things that make us happy when we can.

4   Explain that sometimes the same kinds of things make people happy and sometimes, different things make different people happy. People are usually happier and can do more in life when they are feeling fit and well. How well we take care of our bodies and our health makes a difference to how we live our lives and how happy we feel.

5   Ask the children what kind of things help people to feel fit and well. Write these on the board (exercise, eating a balanced diet, keeping clean, drinking water, having fun).

6   We know that some things such as exercising, drinking water and eating a balanced diet, help to keep us fit and well and this is like charging up a battery so it can keep working. Invite the children to complete Part B of Activity Sheet 28 by writing in the different things that help to 'charge up their batteries'.

Resources

Photocopies of Activity Sheet 28

Extension activities

The children can plant some seeds, taking care of some (i.e. giving them light and water) and leaving some unattended. What happens? (We need to tend to our bodies and health as well.) This can be linked to science activities – compare where our bodies get fuel for power from and what source of power the plants use.

Name .... Date ....

Charged up

Part A

Write all the things you can think of that make you happy on the rays of the sun.

Part B

The picture below shows a battery that is charged up and fully working. What helps you to feel fit and well, or charged up? What kinds of things can you do to make sure that you stay charged up? Write these on the lines coming from the battery.

Blueprints PSHE and Citizenship Key Stage 2 © Judy Hunter and Sheila Phillips, Nelson Thornes Ltd, 2002

Looking good and keeping well

29 Inspector Germ

Aims
- To understand that bacteria and viruses can affect health.
- To develop a sense of responsibility for limiting the spread of bacteria and viruses.

Teaching points
Knowing the theory for this topic is very different to actually putting that knowledge into practice. It is essential to remind children of good hygiene practice in their everyday lives. Gently remind them to wash their hands after going to the toilet and before eating. This means they need access to hot water, soap and towels. Remind them to cover their mouths when they cough or sneeze, to use a handkerchief and so on.

Instructions
1   Raise the following questions:

- Who has heard of the word bacteria or the word virus?
- What do you think the words mean?
- Have you noticed that when someone at home or in the class gets a cold, for example, other people get a cold as well? Why do you think this is?

2   Ask the children in what different ways germs, bacteria and viruses are spread. List these on the board.

3   Discuss the different products they have seen advertised, to help keep ourselves or our homes and environments clean and hygienic. Do they work? Why/why not? (Explain that the different products may help but it depends on how people use them – whether they take responsibility for themselves and others by following basic hygiene routines.)

4   Distribute Activity Sheet 29 and read through Part A The Housefly with the class. Ask the class:

- How do you feel about flies passing on germs and diseases like that?
- Would you know if a fly had landed on your food? (This is why it is important to keep food covered.)

- How would you feel if your friend went to the toilet, didn't wash his/her hands and then put his/her hands into your packet of crisps? Would you know? (This is why it is important that everyone washes their hands.)
- How would you feel if someone sneezed right in your face and droplets of saliva went all over you? (When you sneeze or cough, droplets containing bacteria and viruses can travel up to 5 metres!)

5   Divide the class into small groups and ask them to imagine they have the job of inspecting environments to ensure that hygiene procedures are in place. What would they look for in a kitchen?

6   Review/discuss and give further environments for the children to discuss if time allows, for example public toilets, a fast food bar, a restaurant.

7   Ask the children to complete Part B of Activity Sheet 29. They imagine they are Inspector Germ, who has come to school to check that everyone is following good hygiene rules. Ask them to write on the clipboard a list of what they will look for.

8   Review with the class and draw up a list of good hygiene procedures for the school. (This can be copied on a large sheet for classroom display.)

Resources
Photocopies of Activity Sheet 29

Extension activities
Look at different hygiene procedures in different cultures, for example why do some people eat with their hands and why is this OK? Toilet and washing facilities may be different in different countries. Why is this?

The children can produce hygiene posters for display around the school. Ask them to use their checklist of hygiene procedures and visit different areas of the school, noting what they find. They can report back to the headteacher or school governors. This activity provides links with citizenship.

Inspector Germ

Part A

The housefly

The ordinary flies that you see in your house, and in other places, carry lots of germs and diseases.

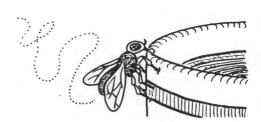

Do you know how?

When the fly lands on a plate, or anywhere else where there may be even a tiny amount of food, it pumps digestive juices (which may include saliva and vomit) on it. This helps the fly to digest the food which it sucks up, leaving behind some of the digestive juices, bacteria and even some of its waste products. If you then eat the food on the plate, this can be transmitted to you! Even if a fly just lands on food, it may carry germs and bacteria on its feet from where it has been feeding before.

Part B

Imagine you are Inspector Germ, who has come to school to check whether everyone is following good hygiene rules. Write on the clipboard a list of what you are going to check in school.

Inspector Germ's Hygiene Checklist

....

....

....

....

....

....

....

....

....

Blueprints PSHE and Citizenship Key Stage 2 © Judy Hunter and Sheila Phillips, Nelson Thornes Ltd, 2002

Looking good and keeping well

30 There are people to help

Aims
- To enable the children to recognise the need to sometimes ask for support.
- To explore who you can ask for help and how to ask for help.

Teaching points
This activity can be usefully linked with the benefits and purpose of a 'mentor' or 'buddy' system in school, if you have one in place. It is particularly important to discuss where to go for help and how to ask for help, prior to transition from first or primary school. It is often difficult for children to understand to what extent they are expected to take responsibility for themselves, and to what extent they can seek support. Be sensitive to the fact that some children feel confident they can discuss anything with their parents/carers whilst others feel this is not an option.

Instructions
1 With the class, collect a list of 'people who help us'. (If you prefer, children can work in small groups to prepare this first.)

2 Discuss with the class which of these people are there to help without you needing to actually ask for help (for example school crossing patrol) and who they might need to approach to ask for help (for example doctor, dentist).

3 Discuss the kinds of things that you would ask the different people to help you with.

4 What are the sorts of issues that it is really difficult to ask for help with or to know who to ask for help? (Discuss the possible options with the children.) Emphasise that some children may feel it is best to talk about any problem with their parents/carers or a family member first, while others may prefer to discuss a problem with someone else.

5 Invite the children to complete Activity Sheet 30 by matching the problem to be discussed with the appropriate person(s). (There may be more than one option for each problem.)

6 Review the activity, discussing the different options the children chose.

7 Ask the class if anyone knows what a 'helpline' is.
- What helplines have you heard of?
- Why is it important for some people to be able to telephone a helpline?
- How might they help?

8 This activity is optional. Prepare a list of helpline numbers with the class, including a sentence about what each one does. It is more beneficial if you include not only national helpline numbers but also local numbers relevant to your particular area/country. (Information can be found in local directories. Your local health support agencies may also be able to supply further details.) Children could prepare some lists/posters for classroom display using their ICT skills.

Resources
Photocopies of Activity Sheet 30

Extension activities
The children can use their ideas for 'people who help us' to make a classroom display. Use this for discussion work around different jobs and what those jobs entail. Explore which children would like to do which job(s) and why. How do their qualities and skills match those required for the different jobs? What targets might they like to set themselves?

There are people to help

Draw a line to join each problem with the person you would go to for help.

My doctor

My dentist

My teacher

A close family member/ older friend

An ambulance driver

Police officer

- Your grandfather falls when you are in the house with him alone. He is unable to move and is in a lot of pain.

- You feel really embarrassed doing PE in school because you are much bigger than everyone else and people stare at you when you get changed.

- You are worried that your teeth are crooked and the top ones seem to stick out too far.

- On your way home from school, some older children keep stopping you. They try to persuade you to buy some tablets. They say the tablets will make you feel great and that you have to try them when you go to the big school or no one will talk to you.

- Everyone in the class is always talking about growing up and how their bodies are changing all the time. You are worried and upset because nothing seems to be happening to your body. Most of the time you don't even know what they are talking about and have to pretend.

- You have been getting into trouble, both at home and at school, for not eating your meals. You seem to feel sick whenever you try to eat something and you just want everyone to stop going on at you about it.

Blueprints PSHE and Citizenship Key Stage 2 © Judy Hunter and Sheila Phillips, Nelson Thornes Ltd, 2002

The environment

31 Look around you

Aims

- To help the children understand that they can contribute to maintaining and developing their local environment or community. (This activity provides links with citizenship.)
- To consider the costs and benefits of spending decisions on the local environment.

Teaching points

The best way to develop awareness of environmental issues and responsible attitudes towards the environment is to provide opportunities for children to put messages into practice. Consider how children are encouraged to save resources in school – water and energy, for example. What is done about keeping the school litter-free? What provision is made to support recycling? This activity can take place over a number of weeks to enable the children to interview their families and neighbours about their ideas and gather more information.

Instructions

1   Ask the children (individually, in pairs or small groups) to think about where their school is situated and to make a list of all the things they like about where their school is and all the things they do not like.

2   Discuss the ideas with the class and agree what are the 'Top 3' best things and what are the 'Bottom 3' worst things. Draw out issues such as what facilities are in the area, whether there is vandalism or crime in the area, whether there are plenty of open spaces.

3   Ask the children to think about where their home is situated and to decide what the 'Top 3' and the 'Bottom 3' things are.

4   Ask the children to work in small groups to discuss the advantages and disadvantages of their local community environment as a whole, and to make a list of all their ideas for improving the environment.

5   Bring the class back together to share their ideas for improvements and to discuss the implications of their ideas, particularly in terms of financial costs and benefits to the local community.

6   Ask the children to go back into their small groups and to agree on one improvement that they would like to make to their local environment. Ask them to consider the following questions and record their ideas on Activity Sheet 31.

- What would the benefits be?
- Who in the community would benefit and why?
- What would be the possible costs of their improvement (roughly)?
- What might be the possible difficulties in making this improvement?

7   Ask the groups to present their ideas to the rest of the class. See if they can agree on what the best idea would be, taking into account all the above factors.

Resources

Photocopies of Activity Sheet 31

Extension activities

The children can prepare interview sheets to gather ideas from their families, friends and neighbours (providing links with maths and ICT).

Link with citizenship: Invite someone from the local council to visit the school and discuss the ideas with the children. This is also an opportunity for the children to learn about the roles and responsibilities of the local council. Instructions 4 to 7 above could be used to help the children to consider their school environment and they could then present their ideas to senior management and governors.

Name... Date ....

Look around you

Write your idea for making an improvement to the local environment.

The idea we have for an improvement to our local environment is:

....

....

The reason we think this is a good idea is because:

....

....

....

The people who would benefit most from this improvement would be:

....

....

To make this improvement money would be needed for:

....

....

....

....

....

£

€

The things that might be difficult in making this improvement would be:

....

....

Remember, it is up to every one of us to look after our environment!

The environment

32 Look into the future

Aims

- To enable the children to consider the longer-term implications of environmental issues.
- To develop an understanding that the environment can be affected by human activity, wants and needs (including their own).

Teaching points

This can be a difficult issue for children to understand. There are clear links with the geography curriculum and you may find it helpful to introduce the children to the topic at a time that coincides with those aspects of the curriculum. There are some good examples of children's literature which can help to broaden the children's thinking and understanding. You can also check for any topical television programmes that you could record to use as snippets for discussion work.

Instructions

1   Discuss with the children all the different uses for trees and wood and record their ideas on the board. (Fruit trees, birds make their nests in trees, used to protect places from the wind, fuel, used for making things, paper.)

2   Wood is very important to us. Discuss where wood comes from. Trees are cut down so we can use their wood. Explain to the children that some countries do not have many trees while others have lots. Can they think of any? (Brazil, Norway, Canada) Countries that do not have many trees depend on other countries for their wood. Some forests are being cut down very quickly. What could happen if they are cut down too quickly?

3   Ask the children (in pairs or small groups) to discuss the different scenarios on Activity Sheet 32.

4   Discuss with the children whether they think we could live happy and healthy lives without using trees and wood in the way we do. Why/why not? Does any one person have a stronger argument than another in the scenarios given? Why/why not?

5   Ask the children to complete the final section of the activity sheet by recording their ideas for making sure we have enough trees for the future.

6   Review and discuss the children's ideas. Ask the children how they could contribute to saving trees, emphasising that everyone has a responsibility to think of the future and play a part in environmental issues.

Resources

Photocopies of Activity Sheet 32

Extension activities

The children can be asked to consider ways of saving resources in school and at home. Discuss how many resources can be recycled and how we can use bottle banks and paper banks, etc. to contribute to recycling. Ask the children to find out what recycling banks are available in their area. Use the same process as above to explore what we need water for and how we can help to save it. Reinforce the message that we need to drink plenty of water to help us stay healthy.

Information

Trees can be divided into softwoods and hardwoods. Most developed countries 'crop' softwoods to make paper. For every tree felled, two or more are planted. Softwoods grow quickly and the overall amount of foliage does not suffer. With hardwoods (such as mahogany) used for furniture and decorative work, the trees grow very slowly and cropping doesn't work. In places such as Brazil and Indonesia, hardwoods are felled and not replaced (or, worse, are burned to make way for pasture). Removal of foliage caused by felling/burning hardwoods (rainforests) means that less carbon dioxide is removed from the air and less oxygen is put into the air, contributing to accelerated global warming and less oxygen to breathe.

Name... Date ....

Look into the future

Discuss why you think trees are important to each of the following people.

Mr Mill "I make paper to sell to people all over the world. Without the trees to do this, schools would not have books, companies would not have paper, envelopes and boxes. We need the packaging for food we buy from shops. It would be inconvenient for many people if I did not produce paper."

Mrs Orchard "I grow trees for fruit, which I sell all over the country. The fruit is sold in supermarkets and greengrocers. I also sell my fruit to manufacturers of tinned fruit. I am helping to feed people and to keep them healthy. Some of the fruit also helps to feed animals. Many people would be disappointed if I didn't grow fruit."

Mr Carpenter "I make things out of wood. Most of the things I make are used to build houses, shops, factories, offices, schools and hospitals. I am helping to give people shelter and places to work in. It would be inconvenient for many people if I didn't make things from wood."

Mr Parkes "I work in a large National Park. I help to look after the trees and woodland. Many visitors come to the park throughout the year. It helps them to get away from the big cities and have some peace and quiet so that they feel better when they go back. They all say how beautiful and unspoilt the park is. Animals and wildlife live in the park. Many people would be disappointed if we did not have parks."

Miss Green "I am a scientist. I carry out research to see what effect cutting down too many trees has on the global environment. I am very worried because it is causing many changes in the earth's atmosphere and in the air we breathe. We need trees to keep the atmosphere balanced and healthy. Everyone will suffer if we continue to cut down too many trees."

Can you think of ways of making sure we have enough trees for the future? Write your ideas below.

....

....

Blueprints PSHE and Citizenship Key Stage 2 © Judy Hunter and Sheila Phillips, Nelson Thornes Ltd, 2002

The environment

33 I want/you want

Aims

- To enable the children to understand that people sometimes have conflicting values and interests in terms of environmental issues.
- To raise awareness that making decisions about the environment can have financial implications.
- To explore the meaning of a democratic decision-making process.

Teaching points

Children need to be given opportunities to discuss issues and understand that different people may want different outcomes in relation to those issues. In a democratic decision-making process they must learn to accept and abide by the decisions made and to take responsibility for their own feelings. This activity has a clear link with citizenship.

Instructions

1 Explain to the class that they are going to imagine there is a problem over a decision about how to spend council tax money. (It would be useful to explore what council tax money is, who pays it, what it is used for.) They are going to work in groups to decide what they think the money will be used for.

2 Divide the children into groups of approximately six. Each member of the group will have one vote. Ask them to decide how they will cast their votes, i.e. anonymously or by a show of hands. What will happen if the vote is split?

3 Allow each group some time to discuss its voting system and then quickly review what they have agreed and how/why they came to that agreement.

4 Distribute copies of Information Sheet 48 and read through the options, ensuring the children understand that they must discuss each one and then democratically decide which of the options they would choose and why.

5 Distribute copies of Activity Sheet 33 for each group to complete. Once they have agreed on an option, they should present their ideas to the rest of the class.

Review by inviting each group to explain what option it has chosen and why.

(You can extend this by then asking the whole class to vote on one final option, if appropriate.)

6 Discuss the following points:

- What kind of things need to be taken into account when making decisions for the local community?
- Who should make these decisions?
- How should the decisions be made?
- Who should pay for improvements to the local community?
- How should the money be collected?
- How much should be spent?

Resources

Photocopies of Activity Sheet 33

Photocopies of Information Sheet 48

Extension activities

Link with citizenship: The discussion questions in Instruction 6 above can also be used to discuss national decision making. Discuss whether there is litter around the school and if so how the situation could be improved. Discuss whether there are recycling facilities in school and if not what could be done. The school caretaker/cleaners could perhaps talk with the children about the litter/damage they see in school and what their job entails.

I want/you want

Voting   How has your group decided they will vote?

....

Decision Which proposal have you chosen?

....

Reasons   Why have you decided on this proposal? (List as many reasons as you can.)

....

....

....

....

Your group How well did you work together as a group?

Did people listen?   ....

How do you know?   ....

....

....

Did everyone join in the discussion? ....

....

....

How did you solve any disagreements? ....

....

....

....

....

Blueprints PSHE and Citizenship Key Stage 2 © Judy Hunter and Sheila Phillips, Nelson Thornes Ltd, 2002

Citizenship

34 It starts with you

Aims
- To understand the balance of individual rights against individual responsibilities.
- To explore what being a member of the school community means.
- To understand how the actions of individuals can impact on the school community and environment.

Teaching points
Whilst it is important that children understand they have rights in society, it is equally important that they understand these rights need to be balanced with responsibilities. This concept is often not emphasised sufficiently. Many of the issues relating to being a member of the school community can be usefully explored through circle work.

Instructions
1. Explore the meaning of the terms 'rights' and 'responsibilities'. Ask the children to give you some examples.

2. Invite the class to think of rights that children and adults have within the school community and write these on the board.

3. Discuss what the implications of these rights might be in terms of responsibilities for individuals, for example everyone has the right not to be bullied, everyone has the responsibility not to bully. Collect ideas for responsibilities on the board.

4. Invite the children to write some of the rights and responsibilities that they feel are most important on the set of scales on Activity Sheet 34.

5. Discuss with the class what kind of problems occur when people in school do not behave responsibly.

6. How do these problems affect the whole school community? (Take, for example, someone leaving the tap on in the toilets and blocking the sink. The consequence of this is that the sink floods. Who does this affect? How? What are the financial implications?) Ask the class for more examples.

7. Discuss what would help people to feel and behave responsibly in school.

Resources
Photocopies of Activity Sheet 34

Extension activities
The children can produce their own 'Charters of responsibility', for example 'In school I am responsible for ...' or, alternatively, they can produce a class charter. Use the 'set of scales' as a method of helping children to develop the skill of decision making – they can weigh up the 'pros' and 'cons' of different problems by writing them on the set of scales. (There are plenty of numeracy links to be explored here.)

Name .... Date ....

It starts with you

On the left-hand side of the set of scales below, write in some of the **rights** that you think are important for people to have in school.

On the right-hand side of the set of scales, write in some of the **responsibilities** that you think are important for people to have in school.

Rights

Responsibilities

....

....

....

....

....

....

....

....

....

....

....

....

....

....

....

....

....

....

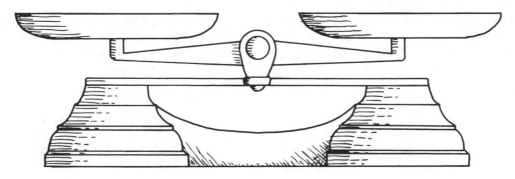

Citizenship

35 It's the law

Aims

- To explore the need to have rules and laws.
- To understand the consequences to self and others of not keeping to rules and laws.
- To explore the concept of justice.

Teaching points

Make sure the children know not only what the school rules are but also why those rules are necessary. When devising classroom rules, make sure the children are fully involved in devising them – you will often find children are far harder on themselves than you would be! It is easier for children to keep to the rules if they fully understand why they are necessary and if they have had the opportunity to discuss them and share their ideas.

Instructions

1   Ask the children:

- What rules do we have to keep when crossing the road?
- What rules/laws do motorists have to keep?
- What rules/laws do we have to keep about caring for each other?

2   What rules/laws do people most often break? (Write the children's ideas on the board.)

3   Take, as an example, the law of keeping to the speed limit when driving and encourage discussion of the following:

- Why do we have laws about this?
- What could happen if we did not have laws about it?
- Why do people break the law?
- What are sometimes the consequences of people breaking this law?
- What do you think should happen when people break this law? Why?

4   As a further example, take the laws of not vandalising property and repeat the discussion points, this time also exploring the following:

- How does this affect both individuals and the whole community?
- Who has to pay when things get vandalised?
- How would you feel if something special that you owned was vandalised?

5   Invite the children to complete Activity Sheet 35, exploring two further issues relating to the law.

Review by inviting the children to share some of their ideas. Discuss the meaning of the word 'justice'. Should people always be punished for breaking the law? Why/why not? Are some laws more important than others? Why/why not? (N.B. Be careful to draw out that even minor laws are there to protect people.)

Resources

Photocopies of Activity Sheet 35

Extension activities

Collect examples (or better still ask the children to collect examples) of newspaper cuttings showing how different laws have been broken. Children can discuss these, particularly examples from their local community, and explore why they think the laws have been broken, what consequences there have been and what they think should happen. They will enjoy acting out some of these situations with class members as a jury. Others can present their case as the law breaker, giving reasons for their actions.

This is a good opportunity to invite a local community police officer to visit the school to build a relationship with the children and answer any questions they may have.

It's the law

The police are trying to find out exactly why some people break the law and how it affects people. They are asking local people about two recent events and ask you to help by completing the two forms below.

A house in your area has been broken into. Many things have been stolen and the property has been badly damaged.

How do you think the people who live in the house are feeling?
....

How do you think the people who broke into the house are feeling?
....

Why do you think the people broke into the house and broke the law?
....

What do you think should happen to the people who broke the law?
....

What could we do to help the people who live in the house?
....

One of the local shopkeepers is finding it very difficult to keep his business running because shoplifters are stealing so much of his stock. It is costing him so much money that he does not know whether he can afford to keep his shop open.

How do you think the shopkeeper is feeling?
....

How do you think the shoplifters are feeling?
....

Why do you think people are stealing and breaking the law?
....

What do you think should happen to the shoplifters?
....

What could we do to help the shopkeeper?
....

Blueprints PSHE and Citizenship Key Stage 2 © Judy Hunter and Sheila Phillips, Nelson Thornes Ltd, 2002

Citizenship

36 I belong

Aims

- To enable the children to explore the range of communities to which they belong.
- To understand the role of voluntary and community groups.
- To raise awareness that people have different cultures, beliefs, interests and abilities.

Teaching points

If your school is a community school, explore the different groups that hold activities within the school and encourage the children to find out more about them. What do people enjoy about them? What do they feel are the benefits of being part of the group? Whose job is it to organise the groups and what does their job involve? If the school supports a particular charity or voluntary group, discuss with the children what the charity does, why it exists and how they depend on volunteers to do different jobs and to raise money.

Instructions

1   Draw a circle on the board with the word 'Me' in the middle of it. Explain to the class that we all belong to different communities and groups. Our lives involve being with many different people in many different situations. Ask them to tell you about the communities and groups they are part of so you can write these in circles around the word 'Me'.

2   Start off by writing 'The people I live with'. (This is easier than 'family' as some children live in different home environments.) Help the children to think of further communities/groups, for example 'My class', 'My school', 'Church', 'City/town', 'Region', 'Country', 'Social groups', 'Sports clubs').

3   Take some examples of the different groups children belong to (for example swimming club, Cubs/Scout groups, drama groups, different church groups) and ask the children to explain to the class what they do in that particular group and what they enjoy about it.

4   Invite the children to complete Activity Sheet 36 by writing in the different groups/communities they belong to and drawing a symbol to represent that group.

Resources

Photocopies of Activity Sheet 36

Extension activities

This activity provides opportunities for links with geography: Where is our city/town? What do we call the region we live in? Which country are we part of? What are some of the special things about our country? Which country do some of my family and friends come from? What are some of the special things about their country? What do we mean by being part of Europe?

Name.. Date ....

I belong

Think of all the different groups and communities to which you belong.
Write them in the clouds.

Next to each of the clouds, draw a symbol which you think says something
about that group or community.

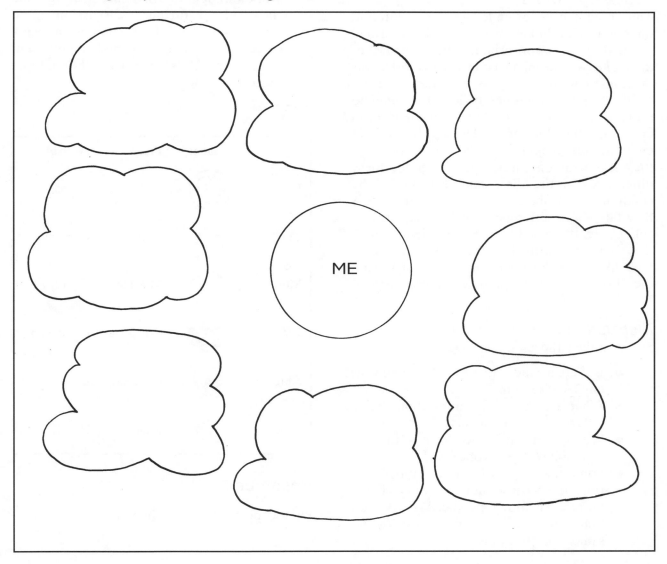

Which group or community do you enjoy being part of the most?

....

What is special about being part of this group or community?

....

How do you help to make the group or community special?

....

Citizenship

37 It's OK to be different

Aims
- To encourage children to respect others.
- To develop an understanding of some of the different beliefs that people have.
- To recognise the views of people of different faiths.

Teaching points
This topic can be extended in many different directions and linked with your RE/Spiritual curriculum as appropriate. The richness of discussion will be enhanced in schools with a mix of ethnic cultures and it is essential for every child to feel that his/her beliefs are equal to everyone else's. It is important for the teacher to encourage the children to develop the skills of empathy and acceptance. If there are children in the class with disabilities, don't ignore these differences in the discussion. Encourage the children to talk about them in the same way as they talk about differences in size, gender, hair colour, etc. If the children are confident enough they can share with the other children what it feels like to have disabilities and in what ways their lives are similar and in what ways different.

Instructions
1   Ask the children the following questions:

   - Is there a child who is exactly the same as anyone else in this class?
   - What are the good things about being different to everyone else?
   - When is it good to have things in common with everyone else?
   - Sometimes people get bullied or ridiculed because they are seen as being different to other people. Why do you think this is, when no one is exactly the same as anybody else?

2   One difference among people is that we believe in different things. People have different religious beliefs or faiths, although groups of people come together to share in their belief.

   Ask the children for names of some religions or faiths. (Record these on the board.)

3   Make a list of different religions/faiths that people in the class have.

   Ask whether some of the children would like to tell the class something about their faith.

   N.B. Where the range of faiths is small (or non-existent) focus on what faiths people have heard of and what they know about them.

4   Work through Activity Sheet 37 with the class, for further discussion and exploration. The sheet contains a blank space in case you have a child of a different faith in the class or in case the children suggest one more.

Answers:

	Symbol	Place	Festival
Buddhist	⚙	Wat	Wesak
Christian	✝	Church	Christmas
Muslim	☪	Mosque	Id-ul-fitr
Jew	✡	Synagogue	Hanukkah
Sikh	☬	Gurdwara	Baisakhi
Hindu	ॐ	Mandir	Diwali

Resources
Photocopies of Activity Sheet 37

Extension activities
Visit different places of worship. Explore the rituals of different religions. Invite parents/members of the local community into school to discuss their beliefs with the children and answer any questions they may have. Use newspaper extracts and video recordings of television news to generate discussion about local and world issues associated with religious beliefs.

It's OK to be different

Some people believe in God and some people do not believe in God. The children below have different beliefs. Their religion is written next to each one of them.

Do you know which symbol from Box A is the symbol for which religion?
Do you know which place of worship from Box B is the place of worship for which religion?
Do you know which religious festivals and celebrations from Box C belong to which religion?
Draw the correct symbol and write the correct place of worship and religious festival alongside the appropriate child.

Box A	Box B		Box C	
	Church	Gurdwara	Diwali	Christmas
	Synagogue	Wat	Id-ul-fitr	Hanukkah
	Mosque	Mandir	Wesak	Baisakhi

Christian ....

Sikh ....

Jew ....

Hindu ....

Muslim ....

Buddhist ....

Blueprints PSHE and Citizenship Key Stage 2 © Judy Hunter and Sheila Phillips, Nelson Thornes Ltd, 2002

Citizenship

38 Read all about it

Aims
- To know how advertising influences supply and demand.
- To explore issues in relation to the care of animals.

Teaching points
The media can have a significant influence on children's thinking. We therefore need to help children to develop the skill of discerning where only one side of an argument is presented or where the media/advertiser may be trying to boost its sales figures through the way it presents a story/product. Be sensitive to the fact that children will have access to different kinds of reading material at home; it is important not to be critical of the newspapers and publications that parents/carers choose. This activity is combined with the care of animals, but if you prefer you can choose a different topic to explore. You may wish to break this activity into separate sessions, depending on the time you have available.

Instructions
1 Read out some simple newspaper articles to the class. Raise and discuss the following questions:

   - What do you think of the article?
   - Does it present all sides of the picture?
   - Is it fair to everyone involved? Why/Why not?
   - Do newspapers always present things fairly?
   - What kind of things do you think newspapers should write about?
   - An excellent means of introducing or reinforcing this topic is to read *The True Story Of The Three Little Pigs* (see page viii for details) which gives the wolf's version of the story.

2 Discuss with the children the different ways that people advertise products.

   Why do people need to advertise?

3 Ask the children to think of television advertisements. What do they remember about them? What do they like about them?

4 Ask the children to think of a product advertised by a famous person (for example a sports person).

5 Ask the children:

   - Why do people advertise products?
   - Do you think it is because they really like the product?
   - Why do advertisers choose someone like a sports star to advertise their products?

6 Explain to the children that they are going to work in groups to devise an advertisement of their own. The aim of the advertisement is to persuade people to care for animals. It should present information in a fair but eye-catching way.

7 Discuss the different ways that we need to care for animals and why this is important.

   Encourage the children to plan their advertisement first, choosing any aspect of animal care. Tell them they can do it by acting out a TV commercial, by producing a poster or leaflet, by devising a radio message and jingle or by producing a page to insert in a newspaper or magazine. (If you prefer, you could give each group a different brief.) They can choose what they like.

8 After the children have prepared and presented their ideas, ask them to complete Activity Sheet 38 as a review of this activity.

Resources
Photocopies of Activity Sheet 38

Newspaper articles

Extension activities
If you have a school bulletin or magazine, this activity can be used prior to involving the children in preparing material for it. Ask the children to note 3 different kinds of TV advertisements and then review what they thought was good and not so good about them. Do the same with newspaper articles. Encourage the children to begin to read newspapers. You could have some available in class and have a weekly 'newsround' as a way of bringing citizenship issues to life.

Read all about it

Describe how you produced your advertisement by answering the following questions.

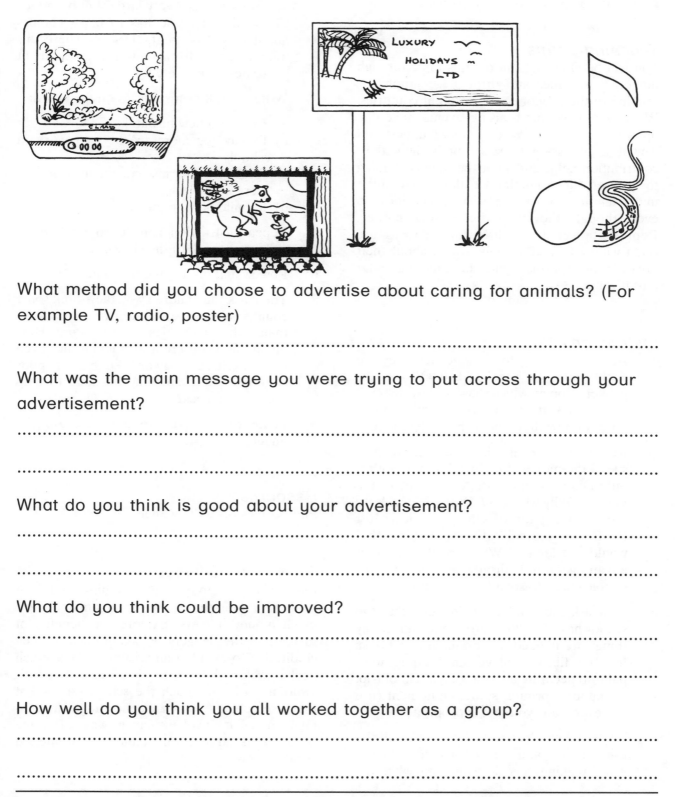

What method did you choose to advertise about caring for animals? (For example TV, radio, poster)

....

What was the main message you were trying to put across through your advertisement?

....

....

What do you think is good about your advertisement?

....

....

What do you think could be improved?

....

....

How well do you think you all worked together as a group?

....

....

Citizenship

39 What can I buy?

Aims
- To understand the costs and benefits of spending decisions.
- To practise the skill of decision making in relation to monetary issues.
- To develop the skill of empathy.

Teaching points
You will be able to reinforce this topic through numeracy activities and through geography by relating to the economics of different countries. When you have fund-raising events, take the opportunity to ensure the children understand why it is necessary to raise funds, how their contribution helps and what the money is going to be used for. Sometimes children have little understanding of what particular charities do even though they may be raising money. Representatives from different charities are often willing to visit schools to talk about their organisation as a whole and what their particular jobs involve.

Instructions
1 Ask the children to imagine that they are each going to receive £10.00/16 euros pocket money which has to last them 2 weeks. Ask them to write down a break down of how they would spend the money.

2 Review by asking what they decided to spend the money on. How did they work it out? Did anyone decide to save any of the money? Why/why not? Did you decide to use the money for something practical? Just treats for yourself? On something that would last longer? What are the different advantages and disadvantages of how people chose to spend the money?

3 Now ask the children to imagine that the school has £500/800 euros to spend. Many things are needed, for example new books for the library, playground equipment, paint to decorate a classroom, a school trip, a computer printer, sports equipment (use however many you feel appropriate).

   Invite the children to make a list of all the things they would need to take into account when making this decision and what the advantages and disadvantages would be for each of the choices, working in groups, individually or as a whole class.

4 Review the above and take a vote on which would be the most popular choice.

5 Finally, ask the children to imagine that the government has a very large sum of money to spend and it too has to make choices about how it is spent. (Discuss where this money comes from, how the government generates money, etc.)

   Write the following choices on the board:

   a) To open a new hospital.
   b) To pay for more teachers to work in schools.
   c) To get more arms and missiles in case there is a war.
   d) To build new motorways.

   Repeat Instruction 3 above from 'Invite the children ... each of the choices'.

6 Review and discuss the outcomes.

7 Then, ask the children why they think some countries in the world are richer or poorer than other countries. Is this fair? How might life be different for them if they lived in a very rich country or lived in a very poor country? Could anything be done to help poorer countries?

8 Invite the children to complete Activity Sheet 39.

Resources
Photocopies of Activity Sheet 39

Extension activities
Ask the children to find out what bills need to be paid in a household and approximately how much money it costs. Explore the benefits of saving and the dangers of taking on too much credit. Try to avoid comparisons of how much pocket money children receive. Raise children's awareness of how much the school equipment they use actually costs and encourage them to take care of it. Involve them in ways of saving waste from an economic and environmental point of view.

What can I buy?

You may have seen pictures of some countries where the people who live there do not have enough money to eat and live comfortably.

Imagine you live in one of those countries and use your ideas to fill in the blanks in the following letter.

Dear ....

Things are very bad for my family here at the moment. There is very little food to eat and every day I ....
....
.... The weather is ....
....

I feel .... and when I watch my mother trying to prepare the little food we have and having to look after all my brothers and sisters, I feel ....
....
....

I would love to go to school but this is not possible because
....
.... I think other countries could help by ....
....

Best wishes,

....

40 Fair treatment

Aims
- To consider why it is wrong for anyone to bully another person.
- To explore strategies for helping when bullying occurs.
- To focus on the skill of empathy.

Teaching points
This topic needs constant reinforcement throughout the school. How you explore the issue with the children will very much depend on the school's anti-bullying policy and it would therefore be inappropriate to be too specific during this activity. Don't forget that bullying by adults is also unacceptable and all staff need to be aware of the importance of modelling fairness and tolerance with the children.

Instructions
1 Ask the children to draw someone who is being bullied and to write some thought bubbles showing what that person is thinking and feeling.

2 Now ask the children to draw someone who is bullying the first person. Ask them to draw some thought bubbles and to write in them what that person is thinking and feeling.

3 Review both drawings with the children, discussing what might have led to the bullying, why the person who is bullying might think it is OK to bully someone else, and what both people's feelings could be.

4 Working in groups or pairs, ask the children to write down all the things that would help to stop bullying happening in school.

5 Use the children's ideas to discuss what kind of things happen in school and where they happen. Together with the children, devise some guidelines/rules to try to stop bullying happening. (Make these positive statements rather than a list of 'don'ts'.) These can be displayed on the classroom wall.

6 Invite the children to complete Activity Sheet 40.

Resources
Photocopies of Activity Sheet 40

Extension activities
If you have not already done so, you may like to establish a 'playground buddy' or 'playground mentor' system which allows children the opportunity to work with their peers and with younger children to support them during playtimes and to help deal with potential bullying situations. Make sure the 'buddies' have sufficient support and be aware of child protection procedures.

Fair treatment

Bullying behaviour is **never** acceptable.

Remember! You have the **right** not to be bullied.
You have the **responsibility** not to bully.

On the shield below, write and draw in things you can do to help make sure that you are never bullied and that you never bully.

My anti-bullying shield

Blueprints PSHE and Citizenship Key Stage 2 © Judy Hunter and Sheila Phillips, Nelson Thornes Ltd, 2002

Moving on

41 Rollercoaster

Aims

- To enable the children to explore their hopes and aspirations for the future.
- To understand some of the changes which take place in human life.
- To understand the range of feelings that can be generated by changes in life.

Teaching points

This activity is most appropriate prior to children's transition at Key Stage 2. Feelings associated with change also link with puberty education.

Instructions

1   Ask the class to think of all the things they have learned to do from the time they were born until now (for example walking, talking, reading, writing) and any changes that have happened to them (for example starting school, new sibling, moving house). Write these on the board, roughly in age order, from birth to the present day.

2   Now ask the children to think of all the possible changes that could take place in their lives between now and adulthood. What do they still need to learn and develop?

3   Discuss some of the emotions that they might experience through these changes – 'ups and downs' that they might feel.

4   Invite the class to complete Part A of Activity Sheet 41 showing the ups and downs of feelings and some of the changes that might occur in their future lives.

5   Focus on some of the changes in relation to the children's future careers. Ask each child to say what their ideal future job would be and why. What do they need to do to help them achieve their goals?

6   Invite the children to complete Part B of Activity Sheet 41, which asks them to set some simple targets in relation to their futures.

Resources

Photocopies of Activity Sheet 41

Extension activities

Invite the children to find out more about their ideal job of the future. What does it involve? What qualifications do they need? Perhaps they could interview someone they know who does that job. Explore job roles and interdependency of jobs within an organisation, for example the different jobs there are in a hospital or in a large department store.

Follow on from this activity by exploring the issues relating to transition from primary school. What are the myths and truths which exist? What are the children's fears and concerns?

Rollercoaster

Part A

The rollercoaster of life. Alongside the rollercoaster below, write in all the changes you can think of that will, or might, happen to you between now and when you become an adult.

Using a different colour, write in the feelings you may experience against the high and the low parts of the rollercoaster.

Part B

Here are three things I will do to help me with my future:

1 ....

2 ....

3 ....

Reviewing progress

The following activities are included to help the children review their progress in relation to PSHE and citizenship issues. Activity Sheets 42–46 can be used at any time you feel appropriate and should be seen as a stimulus for discussion or as a review of discussion, rather than as activities in themselves.

Encouraging children to work together and share their learning, thoughts and ideas is an essential element of the curriculum itself, especially in relation to citizenship and social skill development. Remember PSHE and citizenship need to be 'lived' and there are many more activities that children will take part in that also form part of this curriculum. Children do not, however, necessarily make the connections that adults are able to make, so try to review other aspects of school life as part of PSHE and citizenship; even a five-minute discussion with the class can help children to begin to see the connections. Encourage the children to greet visitors and explain a little about what they have been doing in class. Follow up visits by asking the children to write thank you letters (or emails), and whenever possible involve parents/carers by explaining what their children are doing so they can reinforce the learning at home. Working with parents is important when dealing with health education issues, as the lifestyle they have at home will have a greater impact than the lifestyle they adopt in school.

Review activities

Activity Sheet 42 Dear Martian
Activity Sheet 43 Magic glasses
Activity Sheet 44 We are the champions
Activity Sheet 45 Assembly Instructions
Activity Sheet 46 Amazing, isn't it?

Name.. Date ....

Dear Martian

Imagine a Martian has just landed on Earth and you are the very first person on Earth the Martian meets. The Martian asks you to explain what would be the 'right' way to behave whilst he/she is on Earth and what would be the 'wrong' way to behave.

Write two lists in the spaces below that will help the Martian during his/her visit to Earth.

How should I behave on Earth ?

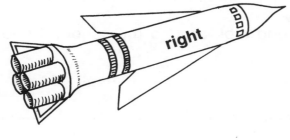

right

wrong

....
....
....
....
....
....
....
....

The most important thing you should do is

....
....

Blueprints PSHE and Citizenship Key Stage 2 © Judy Hunter and Sheila Phillips, Nelson Thornes Ltd, 2002

Magic glasses

Imagine you have been given a pair of magic glasses. When you put them on you can see things differently in the world. Everything is very peaceful. There are no wars or conflicts in the world and everyone cares for each other. What would you see?

When I put on the glasses ⌐⊙⌐ and look around my class, I see

....

....

....

When I put on the glasses ⌐⊙⌐ and look around my school, I see

....

....

....

When I put on the glasses ⌐⊙⌐ and look around my community, I
see

....

....

....

When I put on the glasses ⌐⊙⌐ and look around the world, I see

....

....

....

Blueprints PSHE and Citizenship Key Stage 2 © Judy Hunter and Sheila Phillips, Nelson Thornes Ltd, 2002

We are the champions

Think of all the skills and talents that you have. Write these in the circle opposite.

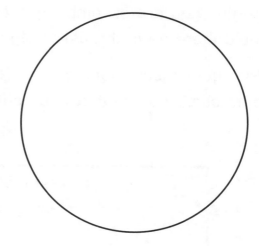

Now think of all the skills and talents that everyone else in the class has. When you combine all of these skills and talents and work together, you can achieve even more.

In the circles below, write all the skills and talents that you and the rest of the class have together.

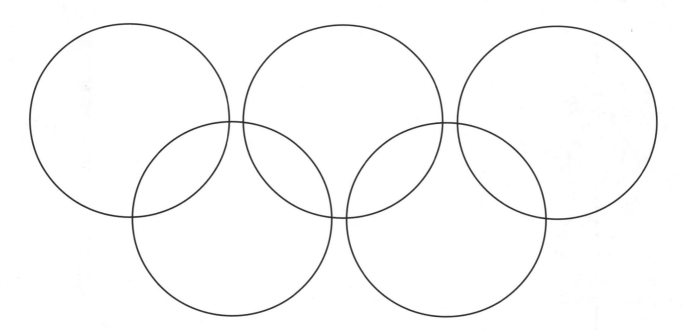

The greatest achievement of this class has been

....

....

Blueprints PSHE and Citizenship Key Stage 2 © Judy Hunter and Sheila Phillips, Nelson Thornes Ltd, 2002

Assembly instructions

Imagine you are assembling a 'Happy and healthy person'. What instructions would there be in the assembly kit for putting that person together?

Write your instructions below. The pictures around the page may give you some clues about what you could include!

**Assembly instructions for a
happy and healthy person**

SPRING WATER

KEEPING
SAFE

zzzZZ

NO
SMOKING

SOAP

Name .... Date ....

Amazing, isn't it?

Read through these amazing health facts. You might find out some amazing facts about yourself.

- Approximately 70 hairs fall out every day, but are replaced when you are young.
- An American woman had hair that was 3.65 metres long.
- The eye muscle moves about 100,000 times a day.
- Perfect eyesight can distinguish approximately 10 million different colours. (Twice as many as the best computer.)
- An average human voice can make itself heard to about 180 metres. (Almost two full-size football pitches.)
- If you peeled off your skin it would weight about 2.7 kg. (Almost three bags of sugar.)
- The enamel that coats your teeth is the hardest substance in the body.
- When you sneeze, particles come out of your nose at up to 100 mph.
- The thickest skin around your body is on the soles of your feet. The thinnest is your eye-lids.
- When digesting your food, it travels 12 metres down a tube in your body.
- If all the veins and arteries in your body were put end to end they would stretch twice around the world.
- The distance between your elbow and your wrist is usually the same as the length of your foot.
- The distance from fingertip to fingertip (when stretching your arms out sideways) is usually the same distance as your height.
- A new born baby needs up to 20 hours of sleep a day, while a 7-year-old needs about 10 hours a day.
- Now write some amazing facts about **you**. What makes you special?

....

....

....

Blueprints PSHE and Citizenship Key Stage 2 © Judy Hunter and Sheila Phillips, Nelson Thornes Ltd, 2002

What is menstruation?

When a girl reaches puberty, she starts to menstruate, which is also known as having periods. This can happen any time between the ages of 8 and 16. A girl knows she has started menstruating because a little blood comes out of the vagina and can be seen on her underwear. Sometimes the blood is a brownish colour and sometimes it is redder. A girl uses a sanitary towel or a tampon to absorb the blood that comes out through the vagina.

Only girls and women menstruate (or have periods); boys do not. It is important, however, that boys understand that this is a normal part of growing up for girls. They should be sensitive to the fact that it can be a confusing and difficult time for girls, in the same way as it can be a difficult and confusing time for boys when they begin to go through puberty and have wet dreams,* for example.

A girl has a period about once every 28 days. The time from the first day of one period to the first day of the next, is called the menstrual cycle. Many girls have irregular cycles when they first start to have their periods. The length of time a girl bleeds for can vary but on average it is about five days. 3–7 days is perfectly normal. Usually the amount of blood coming out of the vagina is quite small (half a small cupful of blood over the 3–7 days). Some girls have some pain or discomfort during their periods and it is best to get advice from a doctor or nurse if this is the case.

The process of menstruation happens because from puberty a girl produces an ovum (egg) every month. This is released at ovulation and moves along one of the fallopian tubes to the uterus (womb). The uterus starts to develop an inner lining which will feed and protect the egg if it is fertilised by a sperm and starts to grow into a baby (if conception takes place). If the egg is not fertilised the lining is not needed so it starts to break up and is passed out through the vagina as menstrual blood.

* Wet dreams – an ejaculation (release of sperm from the penis) during sleep. This is common during puberty and is not harmful.

Blueprints PSHE and Citizenship Key Stage 2 © Judy Hunter and Sheila Phillips, Nelson Thornes Ltd, 2002

I want/you want

There is a problem with a decision over how to spend some council tax money. People have put forward a number of options but there is only enough money to pay for one of the options listed below.

Proposal 1

The local leisure centre needs updating. It is well used by members of the local community and the swimming pool is especially popular. The proposal is to install a fun slide in the pool and improve the changing rooms.

Proposal 2

There is a problem in the area with litter. People are always complaining that it makes the place look untidy and dirty and gives people a poor impression of the area. The proposal is to employ extra staff to keep the area free of litter.

Proposal 3

There has been a great deal of concern about traffic pollution in the town. It is always very busy with so many people coming into the main shopping areas by car and causing traffic jams. The proposal is to use the money to make some parts of the town centre pedestrianised. There wouldn't be enough money to do all of the work needed but it would put the plans in place for future years when more money might become available.

Proposal 4

People in this area do not recycle their waste. The proposal is to use the money to set up recycling facilities in one central area of the town. This would include a bottle bank, newspaper collection, can/metal collection and unwanted clothes collection which will go to a charity.

As a group, discuss the four proposals. Choose the one that you think would benefit the local community the most.

You are going to be asked to present your chosen proposal to the rest of the class. Complete Activity Sheet 33 so that you can explain why you chose your idea and how you came to your decision.

Blueprints PSHE and Citizenship Key Stage 2 © Judy Hunter and Sheila Phillips, Nelson Thornes Ltd, 2002